Man Modified

DAVID FISHLOCK

Man Modified

AN EXPLORATION OF THE
MAN/MACHINE RELATIONSHIP

Funk & Wagnalls / New York

Funk & Wagnalls,
A Division of Reader's Digest Books, Inc.

Printed in Great Britain

CONTENTS

LIST OF ILLUSTRATIONS

PLATES

8

FIGURES

TO MARY
who still believes that medicine
should be left to the doctors

Introduction

MAN today need no longer die. Machines will sustain his heartbeat and breathing — whose failure has always been indicative of death — perhaps indefinitely.

There are machines that can replace kidney function, without which man dies in agony within a matter of days. And where, as with the liver, the subtleties of the natural system still frustrate attempts at simulation, he can be joined through a pump to an animal, even another man, for long enough to reclaim an organ technically dead. He can even be given, with the help of life-supporting machines, vital organs like a heart, 'living mechanisms' harvested from some less fortunate creature.

Until a few decades ago man's relations with machines were remote and uneasy. The connections, chiefly through the hand and the eye, were quickly uncoupled, and much reliance was placed on the adaptability of the human mechanism to accommodate the machine's deficiencies.

In the 1930s the idea began to gain currency of machines that might actually replace men in some roles: Capek's *Robots*, workhorses free from the obvious limitations of the human body, in particular its vulnerability to damage and fatigue. But man, with 20 million years of development behind him, was not so easily displaced. True robots even today are scarce and not very versatile. They have 'development potential', but far less than another concept that has been with us for only a generation. This is the idea of man-machine interaction, a true symbiosis of man and machine, from which is emerging something far more valuable, more exciting than the sum of the two. Man's superb capacity to adapt to circumstances can, when skilfully harnessed to the machine, create a combination of immense power and potential.

The requirements of warfare brought this symbiosis to light, for the Second World War produced a 'quantum jump' in the complexity of weapons systems. The consequences of an intimate man-machine interaction can reach deep into the factory and the laboratory, into commercial and academic life, into the operating theatre, and now into the homes of a rapidly growing number of people.

Man modified by the intimacy of his association with some foreign mechanism, whether a weapon, a computer, an artificial kidney or a transplanted organ, is no longer a rarity. In a few countries the man-machine system promises soon to become commonplace.

Symbiosis between man and machine is something few thoughtful people will be complacent about. The motor car is one familiar machine where man does more than just switch on and switch off. He interacts — through his hands and his feet, through 'the seat of his pants'. Often he forms an emotional attachment too. Psychologically the car can provide its driver with a protective shell that may encourage him to behave quite differently towards the world outside, modifying his personality, sometimes sublimating normal patterns of behaviour and liberating others less tolerant, less socially responsible.

Society, recognizing man's dependence on this machine, has already found ways of manipulating him *en masse* through taxation; and through him the entire economy, by manipulating the industry that builds the machine. Yet society has still to acknowledge the consequences of this interaction on individuals. It examines drivers only for their physical skills, not their capacity to live harmoniously with a complex machine, and with other people in similar circumstances.

Already there is ample evidence that the computer, which offers man the prospect of far closer interaction than the car, can also perturb and distort his responses. Experience of 'time-sharing', in which the computing power of a large machine is shared simultaneously between many users, has already shown the importance of restricting — electronically — a user's right of access to his own programmes, lest the urge to interfere mischievously with those of others should prove overwhelming. The need to guarantee security will grow rapidly as society stores more and more of its confidential data in this way, if the machine is not to offer unprecedented opportunities for interference with the behaviour of individuals.

The motor car and kidney disease claim roughly the same number of people, about 7,000, each year in Britain. There now exists a machine that can replace the kidneys so effectively that it often allows a person, who, through disease or injury, has lost all kidney function and would ordinarily be doomed to an unpleasant death, to regain his health and live virtually a normal life. Normal, that is, except that he must learn to live harmoniously with his artificial kidney.

This is a simple machine, just a programmed pump with a filter, set to purge the bloodstream of poisons the kidneys are no longer able to extract. But man is not built to 'plug into' a machine in this way. Before the surgeon could offer artificial dialysis as any-thing but an emergency hospital treatment some way had to be found of swiftly joining man and machine with far greater intimacy than any car or machine tool requires. The solution was a rela-tively simple coupling of plastic, stitched permanently in place under a local anaesthetic between a convenient artery and vein, in the forearm, for example, through which the blood could be drawn two or three times a week for the machine to purify. The machine itself could then be installed in a hospital or in the man's own home, or brought to his door when required.

The artificial kidney comes remarkably close in performance to the natural organ. But not quite close enough. Deficiencies must be redressed by the man himself, by regular use of a machine two or three times a week, and by meticulous attention to diet, avoid-ing substances—like potassium—the machine cannot handle. Ever present too is the hazard of infection. If man handles his car or computer in a cavalier fashion there is still a good chance he will get away with it, even if someone else suffers, but not if he abuses his artificial kidney. And the scope for abuse is considerable when one part of the machine must be worn permanently.

Nevertheless three of the four patients whom Dr Belding H. Scribner first coupled intermittently to an artificial kidney in Seattle in 1962 were still alive seven years later. They were care-fully chosen—i.e., under forty, free from cardiovascular disease, 'pillars of the community' and contributors to its income.

These will seem particularly stringent criteria, and they have been relaxed slightly now that some hundreds of patients have learned to live in this way. But the consequences of choosing a

15

patient psychologically unsuited to life with a machine were illustrated by the case of a British girl of nineteen who, through her inability to live with the regime that artificial dialysis imposed, spent eight out of seventeen months wholly in hospital. She was, her surgeon concluded, badly selected, lacking the intelligence or will-power to adhere to any strict diet and without the intellectual resources to benefit from such prolongation of life as she had 'enjoyed'. But she was not exceptional. Nearly half the patients attending his clinic would be equally unsuitable, that surgeon believed. His troubles would really begin if ever he had the facilities to treat all-comers.

These are early days yet for a new kind of therapy, but already there has been powerful public pressure for facilities for all-comers: facilities that by one estimate would absorb about 30 million pounds a year in direct costs (and probably far more indirectly in managing the more intractable), and would require a medical staff of over 10,000 to treat 23,000 patients up to fifty-four years of age. And the patients would still be susceptible to a variety of disorders, from infections to psychiatric troubles, that must severely limit their life expectancy. What is more, the coupling of plastic, easily snipped, puts suicide within easy reach.

The obvious solution, not merely to kidney disease but to malfunction of those organs like the heart and the liver, no less essential but for which no artificial replacement yet exists, is the transplanted organ. A heart graft—or indeed the transplantation of any other tissue, including skin—should be seen as the most sophisticated of all forms of man-machine interaction, where the aim is to replace a malfunctioning 'bio-mechanism' with one no less satisfactory than the original in its prime.

But the healthy human body is well protected against the intrusion of material, especially protein material, it has not itself grown. Probably the best we can expect of an inert material is that the body will completely ignore its presence, or that it will slowly absorb it, replacing it with living tissue of its own making. If the body is to accept living tissue from elsewhere, make good the union and keep it nourished and free from infection, some at least of the natural protection must be relinquished.

A plethora of publicity for organ transplantation in the months that followed the first human-to-human heart transplant in

December 1967 established a widespread impression that the basic problems of this type of reconstructive surgery were solved. Subsequent events have shown this is manifestly not so. The human-to-human transfer of living kidneys, first carried out just thirteen years before the first heart transplant, is a much simpler operation, and one that would normally be performed on a patient who is far fitter than the man who needs a new heart. Yet even now half the kidneys transplanted from sources other than a blood relative of the recipient survive less than a year.

Either the recipient rejects the new organ, a form of interaction in which the organ itself can soon suffer irretrievably, or he may succumb to other troubles. These can include the toxicity of the drugs used to suppress the body's defences and harmonize its relations with the new organ, and the risk of infection, even from organisms normally present in the recipient's body, or environment, if those defences are over-suppressed.

If a successful balance is struck between these two hazards, rejection and infection, psychiatric problems—from those of the inevitable dependence on pills (perhaps several dozen a day) to those of 'identification' with someone else's organ—may begin to intrude. Even if all these hurdles are successfully surmounted there remain longer-term consequences, from the organ's disposition to contract the complaint from which its predecessor suffered, to a variety of physiological syndromes ranging from the 'moonface' that accompanies the use of steroids to far more serious consequences—like 'transplant lung'—of long-term therapy with the drugs used to suppress rejection. Most serious of all, there is no evidence yet that the organ transplant is other than a palliative, itself due to fail at best within a few years.

To the responsible surgeon engaged in reconstructive surgery these problems loom large. They are in no degree mitigated by quite another crop of problems that a dozen years' effort on man-made alternatives to the transplant has revealed. One can argue in fact that, since a fundamental problem of biology is involved in the case of the immunological (rejection) response of the body to the ingress of foreign tissue, it is one we may *never* satisfactorily circumvent.

Here then is one sound reason for the pursuit of the artificial organ, the manufactured mechanism that might be worn or implanted, to augment or even replace an ailing organ. Another is that an organ of plastic, unlike a transplanted organ, will be immune to the disease that afflicted the one it replaces. There are also the moral and ethical difficulties a free interchange of human tissues raises for civilized society, especially while they must be used 'fresh'. These are difficulties that it may take a democratic society even longer to resolve than those with which the scientist must contend.

In the case of the heart there is a still more pressing reason, for whereas the mortality from kidney and liver disease is low enough for society to envisage a commensurate supply of donated organs, with the heart this is not so. Britain suffers 15,000 deaths a year from chronic heart disease in people between the ages of twenty and fifty-four alone, and ten times as many all told. In a report early in 1969, the Planning Unit of the British Medical Association concluded that there was no potential supply of heart donors on such a vast scale; a conclusion one can assume would apply equally in any other country.

There is a further reason for pursuing the technology of manufactured organs, namely the relationship they bear to machines the transplant surgeon himself still urgently needs. That the kidney transplant has made so much progress, and has been able to contribute so much experience of finely balanced immunosuppressive regimes to the transplantation of other organs like the heart and the liver, is due in large measure to the existence of the artificial kidney. This machine not only allows the surgeon to restore to good health a patient dying of kidney disease, in preparation for the transplant, but it affords him insurance should he fail to control rejection of the transplanted organ, or should disease re-attack the new organ.

Rejection almost invariably arises at some point in the first weeks of a transplant, and the risk still remains high thereafter. At present the surgeon has only an empirical answer — to increase the dose of the drugs used to suppress this immunological response. Should the rejection reaction still flourish, however, there comes a point where the recipient's health is endangered by oversuppression of his own resistance to infection, and by the toxicity of the drugs themselves. Before this point is reached, the surgeon will remove the rejected organ and revert to treatment by the artificial kidney, preparatory to another attempt at transplantation.

No such insurance exists when a transplanted heart, lungs or liver begins to be rejected. In these cases the surgeon has no option but to give more and more drugs, with results that are now reflected in the high mortality of heart recipients.

It was the heart-lung machine, perfected in Britain in the late 1950s, that made open-heart surgery possible in the first place. But this machine is still too harsh on the blood to serve except in

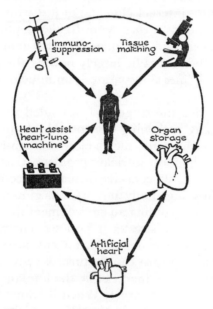

FIG. 1. The four problem areas that hold the key to
transplanted organs

the operating theatre. A more robust machine that none the less handles blood much more gently is needed as a heart bypass to which the heart-transplant surgeon might revert, so avoiding the need for excessive immuno-suppressive measures. But a satisfactory solution to this difficult engineering problem would also be an important contribution to the problem of storing living organs for at least a few days, alleviating the unseemly scramble to 'cannibalize' the dead and giving the surgeon time to ensure a much closer match between the transplanted organ and its recipient. Ironically enough, a 'gentle' heart-lung machine would also go far towards solving the technical problems of making an artificial heart.

These two branches of reconstructive surgery, transplantation and implantation, far from being mutually exclusive, even in competition as some surgeons have sought to establish, are really complementary, as Fig. 1 tries to show. The four key problem areas of immediate concern to organ transplantation—immuno-suppression, tissue matching, storage of organs, and an artificial circulation system—interact closely, not just with the patient but with one another, and in turn with the development of artificial versions of the heart and the lungs. What is more, the solutions to these key problem areas lie largely outside the province of the surgeon, with disciplines as disparate as immunology and hydraulic engineering.

The engineer, like the surgeon, has tended to minimize difficulties that by any reckoning are formidable in attempting to bring man and machine into such a close relationship. Men accustomed to solving the most intricate problems that aerospace and weapon technology could conceive turned with confidence to those of medical engineering. Only now is it beginning to dawn just how complex and demanding an environment the living body can be; how severe are the stresses it imposes, chemically and biochemically as well as mechanically, on any intrusion; and how easily that intrusion in turn can perturb the environment. Above all, they now realize how inaccessible the human mechanism can be to mend, or even to measure. When it comes to the capacity of living material for self-repair, for self-energizing, even for shifting the inevitable accumulations of bacteria, the engineer finds he cannot begin to compete.

The conclusion must be that if society really wants a successful symbiosis between man and machine with the degree of intimacy implicit in an organ transplantation or implantation—and there is powerful evidence that it does, from public reaction to the first attempts to implant an artificial heart in 1966, and to transplant a heart in 1967–8—it must adopt a systems approach to the subject. It must recognize the problem as multifaceted, embracing matters of moral, ethical and legal concern as well as technical

20

complexities like the nature of the immunological response or the design of a pump that will not damage blood, and organize things so that every facet, 'logistics' included, is tackled simultaneously.

For some years past, leading surgeons have been deeply worried by some of the consequences of the more adventurous lines they were pursuing in reconstructive surgery. The more thoughtful knew they were fast getting out of their depth; that by solving the simplest of the many problems, the surgical techniques of transplanting or implanting, they were exposing problems of far greater complexity. In particular they were baffled by the social problems —for example, the moral and ethical consequences of cannibalizing one human body, dead or alive, to assist another. Even matters on which the medical man has traditionally pronounced verdict, such as the precise moment of death, were being called into serious question by the need to cannibalize quickly, before the coveted tissue itself started to die.

Questions of this kind have now been brought into the public arena for serious discussion. There are others, however, that society has scarcely begun to consider, one of which is the economic consequences of success. It is quite possible that a co-ordinated effort to supply the knowledge and the technology the transplant surgeon lacks today could meet with success for a sum that was very modest by comparison with the cost of a new weapon or defence system, and more quickly than the seven years or so that normally elapses between concept and final delivery in this field. But even the world's wealthiest nations may balk at the cost and consequences of making man's most intimate interaction with the machine available to all-comers—especially if it should prove no more than a palliative measure for the desperately sick.

Modified man, far from being a person to be feared, shunned or despised—or even pitied—should be man for whom life has been enriched; enhanced by the skills of surgeons or engineers, physicists or chemists, often all four and others in concert. It is my aim to show not only that this is so, but how it is done, or is going to be done. And, of course, to indicate the pitfalls.

Medicine, they say, is the oldest technology. The basic theme of this book is a brand-new technology, man-machine interaction, the symbiosis of man and machine at every level of sophistication up to the enhancement of living functions. It is a quest upon which some of the world's greatest companies, its most fruitful research centres, have embarked. Yet with all their resources it is one that very often baffles the best brains. No environment is more stubbornly resistant to penetration, even for measurement, or more infuriatingly aggressive when faced with intrusion, than that of the body. But its defences are now being breached. And breached more rapidly than man can accustom himself to the changes he is now bringing about.

CHAPTER ONE

Man Measured

'Human beings don't come with convenient test points.'
Dr Robert F. Shaw

MEASUREMENT—precise observation—is the foundation of all science, but it was late in being applied to the human body; which tends to account, of course, for the relative backwardness of medicine as a science. But to be fair, observations and measurements are not easily made on the living body, as the Italian physician Sanctorius (1561–1636) must have decided during the long nights he spent on his scales, recording the incomings and outgoings of his own body.

The engineer can apply the most ruthless tests and methods of examination to his creations before they will suffer. He can irradiate them with quantities of X-rays or gamma-rays or ultra-sound that would rapidly kill living cells, to penetrate solid structures and illuminate the flaws. The doctor or surgeon, on the other hand, must always work on the basis that anything he does to the patient should not make him worse and perhaps will make him better. If the 'experimental animal' happens to be a normal healthy person, about whom we need urgently to know much more, the medical man must be very careful indeed not to impair his health.

The difficulty has been how to make meaningful measurements on so complex a mechanism without at least greatly inconveniencing the subject. If the subject is sick, he becomes captive; but no longer is he a normal person who can be expected to perform in a normal manner. The general rule of medical men has been not to expect others to undergo an experience on their behalf they would not undergo themselves, and for this reason most research workers initially perform clinical tests and measurements only upon their own bodies and those of their research assistants.

Other sources of human 'experimental animals' have been used from time to time. Doctors in Nazi Germany, for example, were permitted to use the inmates of concentration camps, but the evidence is that for all the suffering they inflicted upon these people their scientific technique was so poor that little or nothing emerged that was not already known or could not have been discovered without using a living subject.

Even today there are people who believe that convicts, especially the criminal lunatic, and even conscientious objectors, should be compelled to lend themselves to science. On another level, destitute persons in the U.S.A. can acquire a measure of care and attention in exchange for freedom of access to their bodies. This is not, of course, to say that they risk loss of sexual privacy; although two American research workers, William Masters and Virginia Johnson, of the Reproductive Biology Research Foundation in St Louis, have induced some people who consulted their clinic with problems like infertility and sexual inadequacy to collaborate in their exhaustive investigations into the physiology of the sex act.[1]

In this case there is evidence that such people sometimes actually benefited from the collaboration, and although some of the experiments involved a plastic penis, mechanically driven in a way that could be controlled by its female partner, making it possible for scientists to take photographs and make measurements, there is no suggestion that the women were exposed to the slightest risk or inconvenience.

Other experiments, however, have put their subjects at risk, as Dr M. H. Pappworth points out in *Human Guinea Pigs*.[2] His search through a portion of the medical literature of recent years has yielded a wealth of evidence that experiments are made freely by a small number of medical research teams in the U.S.A. and Britain, on the sick and dying, on geriatric patients, on criminals, even on infants and pregnant women.

The astronaut, on the other hand, provides physiologists with an almost perfect experimental animal: intelligent, highly trained and disciplined, and in the peak of physical condition. Moreover, he is a captive animal in the sense that he must work closely with his craft, which can therefore be used to collect large amounts of information and, if need be, relay it back to the ground for continuous analysis. Dr Charles Berry, Director of Medical Research Operations for the United States' National Aeronautics and Space Administration, gives the medical objectives of the manned space-flight programme in these terms: To provide medical support for man, enabling him to fly safely in order to discover (1) how long man can be exposed to the spaceflight environment without greatly upsetting his body or its performance, (2) what causes the changes observed, and (3) whether preventive measures or treatment are needed and, if so, what is best.

Curiously enough, however, the astronaut is no more capable of determining his own capacity or of assessing any deterioration in his performance than is a sick person. There are plenty of examples of the failure to recognize and heed warnings of fatigue when a person is concentrating hard upon a task. The inquiry by the Civilian Accident Board following the crash of a 'space glider' in May 1967 concluded that ' ... the pilot was overburdened in his normally exacting landing task with the M2 vehicle as a result of events which left him disoriented, distracted and without the customary height cues.' For this reason alone it is important that the performance of the astronaut be monitored continuously and accurately; the outcome of which has been a considerable volume of information about the human mechanism, some of which we shall discuss later in this chapter.

But it works the other way too. Writing in the journal *Science* a few years ago, the eminent physiologist Dr John S. Gray remarked that he had been asked what happens to a physiologist when he ventures across the frontier into engineering. 'Judging from my own experience,' he said, 'I think the result can be expressed in two sentences. The physiologist is not apt to become an engineer, for, as the saying goes, you cannot make a silk purse out of a sow's ear. But the physiologist can learn from engineering an enormous amount of pure physiology that he cannot learn from any other source.'[3]

Not many are so venturesome. As a materials scientist with a passion for imitating the materials of nature once put it to me, 'No biologist believes that engineering applies to biology.' That it should, and does, is the contention of this book. The implications of accepting this simple fact are immense for engineering, where the proper understanding of biological systems can yield dividends in areas as disparate as tough materials and nimble manipulators, machines that will reason and those that will recognize patterns.

But the greatest implications of all are for the future of man himself, whose activities and behaviour and performance are coming increasingly to depend upon subtle interplay between the human mechanism and machines of widely varying complexity.

Bio-medical engineering is the inelegant title of this new inter-discipline of science, but there is nothing inelegant about its methods or its achievements. In preparation for subsequent chapters that discuss man's union and interaction with man-made mechanisms, let us examine some of the major sub-systems of the human mechanism and the methods used to measure them.

LIVING MECHANISMS

The human mechanism operates through the activity of various flow systems, the most important of which is blood, the fluid that keeps the mechanism refuelled and repaired. The description that follows of this all-pervading fluid system and its manifold sub-systems, and of the complicated ways in which they interact and interdepend, will do no more than briefly introduce the reader to some of the statistics of physiology with which the engineer attempting to enter this field must contend.

The circulatory system is a network of channels from just over one inch, about the size of a garden hosepipe, down to one-fifty-thousandth of an inch in diameter, totalling some 60,000 miles in length. It permeates the tissues with such thoroughness that no cell in the body is more than one-fortieth of an inch away from a capillary, the smallest of the blood vessels.

Through these channels flows a fluid, nearly five litres in volume, or 7·7 per cent of the body weight. Its primary purpose is to keep every cell in the body constantly replenished with nutrients and simultaneously to flush away the waste products — the effluent — of metabolic processes. So we find the fluid we know as blood differing significantly in its composition depending upon the part of the human mechanism from which it is sampled. It is essentially a transport medium—of an unusually sophisticated kind.

This medium is composed of plasma and living cells in roughly equal proportions by volume. Plasma is a weak brine that contains many other chemicals in solution and suspension; some impart a particular physical or bio-chemical property, an osmotic pressure or the ability to clot when exposed to air, for example, while many others are merely in transit from one part of the body to another. The living cells, also in suspension, are much larger than the chemicals suspended in plasma—so much so that the red and white cells must pass in single file through the capillaries.

The presence of these cells accounts for the sensitivity of blood to damage, mechanical damage especially, which can rupture the cell walls, and inclines the physiologist to regard blood almost as an organ in its own right. As we shall see later, it raises difficulties for the engineer desirous of pumping or artificially oxygenating the fluid, and for the designer of a blood valve, for the heart for example.

The blood is kept constantly in motion by a pump that normally pulsates some sixty or seventy times a minute, each time ejecting about 100 millimetres—say, six litres of blood a minute. When called upon, however, the pump's output can increase five-fold in volume at very short notice, and moreover without damage to the fluid it is handling. Arrest this pump and parts of the brain will begin to die within a matter of minutes.

The heart is actually a double pump: some 300 grams of cardiac muscle enveloping parate four sechambers, the two atria (auricles) serving to receive the blood, and the two ventricles to expel it through separate circuits of the system (see Fig. 2). Cardiac muscle is a special kind of muscle with a prodigious capacity for hard work. In the course of twenty-four hours it contracts about 100,000 times, squeezing some 14,000 litres of blood from the ventricles. With the body at rest, the heart accounts for 11 per cent of its production of heat.

To sustain a normal energy output of 1·5 to 4 watts, rising to around 7 watts—about one-hundredth of a horsepower—with vigorous exercise, the heart muscle itself demands up to a tenth of the heart's own output of blood. Any impediment to this heavy flow through the coronary arteries can rapidly prove disastrous for muscle as highly taxed as the heart.

The two circuits of the haemodynamic system the heart supplies are sketched in Fig. 3. One feeds the lungs alone, and the other the rest of the body. The supply to the lungs is of blood depleted in one important respect, oxygen.

Oxygen is replenished by diffusion, a process that is essentially mechanical. The lungs are simply membranes of enormous area, about a hundred square metres, most compactly arranged in the

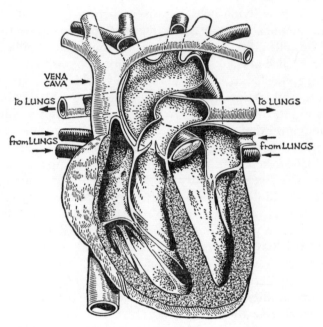

FIG. 2. The heart: a 'gentle pump' comprising some 300 grams of cardiac muscle, with an output of about 14,000 litres a day

form of millions of minuscule pockets, called alveoli. On one side of this membrane is air at atmospheric pressure; on the other, the capillary blood, low in oxygen, supplied by the pulmonary artery.

The blood is recharged by the greater pressure of oxygen in the air outside. Oxygen makes up 20·95 per cent of the atmosphere, but only 16·4 per cent of exhaled air. At the same time, the blood is relieved of most of its carbon dioxide, one of the body's principal effluents, by a similar process of diffusion across the membrane

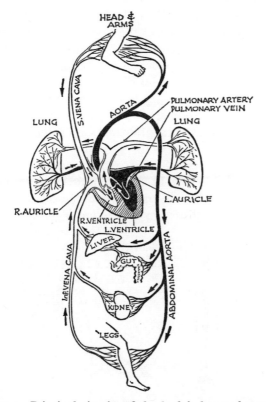

FIG. 3. Principal circuits of the body's haemodynamic
system

brought about by the much lower pressure of carbon dioxide in
the atmosphere. Carbon dioxide accounts for 4 per cent of exhaled
air, one hundred times as much as the atmosphere contains.

The blood is treated by another process, filtration, one of the
most commonplace of processes in chemistry. This is the practice
of separating one phase from another—a solid from a liquid or
liquid droplets from a gas. In the kitchen it is called straining, a
crude process that uses metal or nylon sieves. In the body it is a
two-stage process, a 'straining' of the blood to remove almost
every molecule smaller than the red blood cells, followed by a
selective resorption of the filtrate that returns many valuable
substances to the bloodstream.

The agents of filtration are the kidneys, two organs flanking the spinal column, suspended from the rear wall of the abdomen. Their primary purpose is to rid the body of excess water and the waste products of metabolism by continuously filtering the blood; but they have more subtle roles in regulating the composition of the body fluids and the arterial blood pressure. In their absence the body can survive no longer than a few days.

Each bean-shaped organ, some four inches in length and weighing about four or five ounces, offers about a square metre of filter surface to the bloodstream, in the form of a million minute 'filter funnels', the nephrons (see Fig. 4). About a quarter of the heart's output, approximately 1·3 litres a minute, goes straight to the kidneys, where an elaborate haemodynamic scheme sustains the blood pressure at a high level right down to the capillary bundle

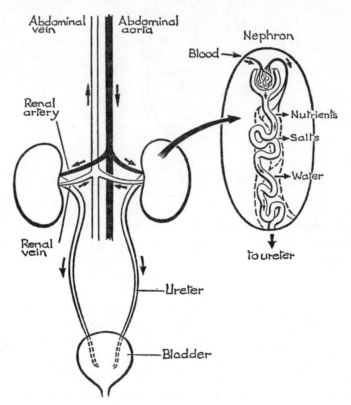

FIG. 4. The kidney: 120–150 grams of tissue that offers the blood about a square metre of surface for dialysis

serving each nephron. Wholesale transfer of fluid and small molecules then takes place in the 'cup' of the nephron, to deliver what is essentially blood plasma—blood from which the red corpuscles and larger protein molecules have been strained—at the rate of 120 millilitres a minute, or, say, 170 litres a day: twice the weight of a large man.

Far more sophisticated, however, are the processes that occur in the 'stem' of the nephron, where 99 per cent of the water along with sodium chloride, vitamin C, amino-acids and glucose are re-absorbed by the blood, and other substances leached from it. Osmosis is the process at work here. Differences in the concentration of solutions on either side of a special kind of membrane, called a semi-permeable membrane, set up an osmotic pressure that transfers fluid from the weaker into the stronger solution. This is the mechanism by which all living cells supplied with nutrients are relieved of their waste products. Since it depends crucially upon osmotic pressure—the 'back pressure', or force that is just sufficient to arrest fluid transfer by osmosis—it is plain that any marked change in the composition of the body fluids must have a profound physical influence upon every cell in the body.

The 'stem' of each nephron, then, is formed from a semi-permeable membrane across which there is a two-way transfer of substances between the bloodstream and the coarsely filtered plasma in the nephron at an effective pressure of about forty-five millimetres of mercury. This serves to concentrate the fluid to about 1 per cent of its original volume. The process is controlled by a number of hormones.

This leaves from 1 to 1·5 litres a day of a slightly acidic solution of urea, uric acid, phosphates, creatinine, sulphates, bacteria, and so on, to be pumped by peristaltic contractions along the ureter to the bladder. The volume and composition of urine is a valuable source of information about the performance of the kidneys, and indeed about the body as a whole. One important reason why the kidney has been adopted as the prototype for organ transplants (see Chapter 5) is the ease with which its function can be assessed by examining its output.

The *cardio-vascular* system, as the blood circuit is called, is our internal life support system, yet one of which we still know very little. But the incidence of cardio-vascular diseases has risen alarmingly with increasing affluence, accounting for more than half the total number of deaths among Americans each year.

One of the difficulties in learning more, quite plainly, is to penetrate the circuit without upsetting the elegant flow patterns therein, and without damaging the delicate fluid it is handling. The doctor usually contents himself with measuring blood pressure and with a check on the sounds the heart itself is making. There are two sounds, primarily: one caused by the closing of the valve flaps between the low-pressure atria and the high-pressure ventricles when the heart relaxes after a contraction, and the other by the closing of the outlet valves from the two ventricles. So the sound — 'lub-dup' — the doctor hears from a healthy heart is repeated at each heart-beat. Should disease have damaged the valves or narrowed the aorta, however, perturbations in the flow of blood will produce telltale sounds or 'murmurs' as well.

In addition, the doctor can learn a lot from the electrical activity of the heart. The rise and fall of this electrical activity with the pulsations of the organ give rise to a characteristically shaped curve, known as the electrocardiogram or E.C.G., which disease may distort. The E.C.G. can be recorded through electrodes attached to the skin without need to penetrate the body.

Other techniques require penetration of the blood circuit. One now practised (although not without risks, as Pappworth points out in *Human Guinea Pigs*) is designed to help the radiologist obtain a clearer X-ray picture of the heart. This is the admission of a catheter — a long, narrow tube of rubber or plastic — that is passed along an artery until it enters the left atrium, where it injects a drug or a contrast medium. Recent progress in miniaturizing the strain gauge — a device whose electrical resistance is altered by stresses and strains — promises to permit its introduction in this way, so that pressure measurements might be made precisely where they are wanted.

Then there is the 'pod', described by a team of Israeli scientists, led by E. H. Frei of the Weizmann Institute, to the sixteenth Conference on Engineering in Medicine and Biology in Baltimore in 1963. The pod is a remotely controlled capsule designed to zip through the larger ducts of the body such as the major blood vessels or the urinal tract at speeds of a foot a second, by lashing its tail in response to a rapidly changing magnetic field arranged outside the body. The pod can also be used to introduce a catheter or a drug or, to quote its inventors, 'perhaps, in the future, a surgical micro-device'.

But none of these techniques approach the business end of the system, the interfaces across which substances are transferred into and out of the blood circuit, through membranes only microns* in thickness. There is good reason to believe that several diseases can first be detected from aberrations in the capillaries, while some cardio-vascular diseases may even originate at this level.

Activity in the capillaries—the micro-circulation, as it is called—can be observed under the microscope, but this is a long way from direct measurement. Professor George Bugliarello, a civil engineer who is also chairman of the bio-technology committee at the Carnegie Institute of Technology, and a man who believes that living systems hold the solution to many present-day engineering problems—'Almost invariably biological flow systems conform to good engineering practice ... ' he once told a symposium of chemical engineers[4]—has adopted a traditional engineering approach. He has constructed a large-scale model of a capillary.

This model is actually a towing tank, of the type used in ship design, in which Bugliarello is studying drag characteristics and changes of shape of very large models of the deformable red blood cell. The tank itself is about three feet square and sixteen feet in length, with walls that are transparent (see Plate 1), and filled with glycerine to simulate blood. Through this fluid are towed large models, several inches across, of the red blood cell.

Nor are the prospects for penetrating the capillaries themselves so remote, when one recalls the sensitivity of instruments developed in the past few years for space research. As Dr Benjamin W. Zweifach of the New York University School of Medicine remarked at an aerospace conference in Boston in 1966 in a paper on 'The utilization of space technology in the fight against cardio-vascular disease': 'The space technologist has developed a remarkable array of instrumentation ... to deal with orders of magnitude below even the quantities of energy which circulatory research specialists would like to monitor on regular and systematic basis.' The space scientist can already detect and record with discrimination

---

* A micron is one-thousandth of a millimetre, or 40 millionths of an inch.

the billionth of a billionth of a watt of electromagnetic energy emanating from the *Mariner IV* spacecraft, by techniques that could be adapted to follow fluctuations in the flow of blood through microscopic vessels, or patterns of electrical activity in the brain—without ever penetrating the system itself.

A Swedish professor of anatomy, Dr Per-Ingvar Branemark, has hit upon the idea of implanting a window in the arm of a subject, so that he can peer through his microscope beneath the skin to examine the capillaries. He buries a quartz disc, mounted in a frame of titanium, in the arm of his subject. In this way he can follow, for hours at a stretch, the flow of blood through capillaries only ten microns in diameter.

It is the role of the skeleton to support these and other systems, protect them, and, through a system of levers, afford them mobility. An engineer would almost certainly choose a metal for the purpose. Nature, which employs no metal as such, has fashioned the skeleton from far less likely substances: inorganic compounds, which in the case of human bone include up to 60 per cent of calcium phosphate.

'From the engineer's point of view,' observed D'Arcy Thompson half a century ago, 'bone may seem very weak indeed; but it has the great advantage that it is very nearly as good for a tie as for a strut, nearly as strong to withstand rupture, or tear asunder, as to resist crushing.'[5] In this respect it is akin to mild steel, the most commonplace of all engineering materials. Bone is half as strong as mild steel, although only one-third of its weight.

Unfortunately, most of the early investigations of bone were carried out by medically trained research workers who, to quote one engineer who recently began to explore its properties, wouldn't recognize a stress and were obsessed by the bio-chemistry—to the neglect of the load-bearing aspects. Quite recently, however, there has been a surge of interest in bone as an engineering material. This appears to have revealed one major complication, in that no one is quite sure yet whether the properties of living bone may not differ substantially from those of a bone that has been removed from the tissues that nourish it. There is even a theory that bone is strengthened hydraulically, on demand, perhaps by an arrangement that 'pumps up' the bone with fluid to increase its stiffness.

One of the most comprehensive surveys of the physical and

mechanical properties of bones (and other tissues) has been in progress since the late 1930s in the Department of Anatomy of the Kyoto Prefectural University of Medicine in Japan, where Professor Hiroshi Yamada leads work that he plans to publish in the

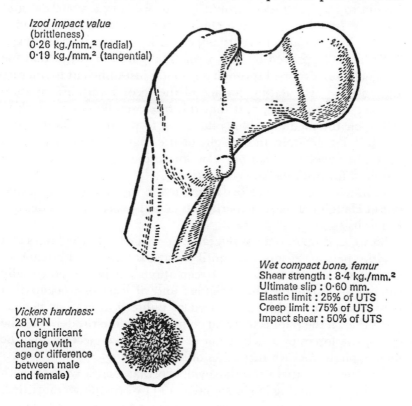

Izod impact value
(brittleness)
0·26 kg./mm.² (radial)
0·19 kg./mm.² (tangential)

Wet compact bone, femur
Shear strength : 8·4 kg./mm.²
Ultimate slip : 0·60 mm.
Elastic limit : 25% of UTS
Creep limit : 75% of UTS
Impact shear : 50% of UTS

Vickers hardness:
28 VPN
(no significant
change with
age or difference
between male
and female)

Cleavage strength greatest at age 20-30, 9·0 kg./mm.².
9% reduction in cleavage strength by age 60-70.
Female strength, 90% that of male bones.

FIG. 5. Some physical properties of human bone, measured by scientists with the Kyoto Prefectural University of Medicine in Japan

U.S.A. in 1969.[6] These investigations, highly regarded by British scientists, have yielded much information on the engineering properties of human bone. Some of these properties are summarized in Fig. 5.

A convincing if macabre illustration of the strength of the

human skeleton is provided by the difficulty in abruptly terminating life by the process of hanging. It was pointed out by an Irishman, the Rev. Samuel Haughton, that unless the quite considerable force of 2,240 foot-pounds is administered to the neck by the rope, the shock is insufficient to fracture a vertebra, and death by hanging becomes a clumsy, protracted and painful procedure, brought about eventually either by apoplexy or asphyxia.

'It has been proved by me', wrote Haughton in 1873, 'that the shock of a ton dropped through one foot is just sufficient to fracture the anterior articulating surface of the second vertebra at their contact with the atlas, and that this fracture allows the shock to fall upon the medulla oblongata, so as to produce instantaneous death.'[7] By dividing the weight of the 'patient' in pounds into 2,240, he concluded that one can obtain the length of 'long drop' required for instantaneous execution.

I am told there was a story recounted in the bars of Dublin that one of Haughton's early experiments actually succeeded in decapitating its subject.

So we find there is a considerable safety factor in the bones of a healthy person, at any rate until his age is fairly well advanced. Of course, there are plenty of recreational activities potentially capable of damaging the skeleton; and at least one occupation now constitutes a risk. The speed of military aircraft is now so great that, if the pilot is to avoid collision with the rudder when he ejects, the forces of acceleration of an explosive ejection may be high enough to crush the bones of his spine.

But there is circumstantial evidence that bones weaken with age, both by thinning in cross-section and by becoming embrittled, while the problem of degenerative diseases that attack the joints, such as rheumatism and arthritis, are too well known to need emphasis. Arthritis is responsible for the loss of 130 million working days a year in Britain, only 2 per cent of the inhabitants of which can expect to avoid some form of the disease by the age of seventy, according to a WHO survey. Plainly, there is no great merit in devising sophisticated means for keeping organs at work in a body that is seizing up solid or growing too weak to support them.

Probably the most thoroughly investigated of the joints in the human skeleton are the hip joints, each of which takes the body's full weight about one thousand times in the course of walking a mile. Perhaps there is no better example of the inaccessibility of certain parts of the human mechanism even to microminiaturized instruments, than the hip joint, linchpin of the human gait. Its function is complex and difficult to analyse, and the slightest fault in its performance is amplified by the levers of the leg to affect the rhythm of the gait. Its performance therefore is usually assessed indirectly, by the cine camera and from measurements made on 'walkways' or force platforms that work in much the same manner as a weighbridge. Simpler and more versatile, however, is the idea of Dr John Scales of the Institute of Orthopaedics in London, who conceived a sandal that would radio back its information, leaving the patient's movements relatively unhampered.

This load-measuring sandal, developed in 1967 by instrument engineers with the Royal Aircraft Establishment, has a sole built up from lacy sheets of metal foil sandwiched between layers of sponge rubber. As pressure is applied the sponge compresses, so reducing the electrical capacity of the structure, itself part of an oscillator. In this way the broadcasting frequency of the sandal is arranged to depend directly upon the load imposed by the patient. Signals from the sandals are picked up by an aerial around the room, amplified and separated to distinguish right and left legs.

Mr N. Rydell has reported measurements he made on two patients, male and female, in whom he had implanted prostheses to replace their fractured femurs.[8] The joints were provided with small strain-gauges. Once his patients were walking again the electrical leads from these strain-gauges were brought out through the skin, allowing Rydell to record joint forces as great as 4·33 times the body weight (for the woman when running).

Mr J. P. Paul of the Bio-Engineering Unit at the University of Strathclyde in Scotland has described another technique for measuring the forces transmitted by human joints to a symposium on 'Lubrication and wear in living and artificial human joints' in London in 1967.[9] He measures the force exerted by the foot upon a plate and correlates it with cine films taken from the front and the side of the subject, and also with 'myoelectric' or muscle signals that indicate which muscle groups are participating in a particular motion. Paul has found the greatest stresses on joints — 3·9 times the body weight on the hip and 3·4 times the body weight on the knee—to be exerted at periods of low relative velocity.

Even when the measurements are to be made on the outer surface of the body there may be serious difficulties, as is the case with measurements so apparently simple as length and size. Another aerospace technique, photogrammetry, is proving invaluable here. This is a very accurate method of stereo-photography that has been developed to its most advanced form in the interests of aerial and satellite reconnaissance. Used at close range, however, photogrammetry has undertaken physiological tasks as disparate as the mapping and measurement of the Great Buddha at Kamakura, a 120-tonne statue over 12 metres high, with an accuracy of a few millimetres over its entire surface, and mapping of the contours of a living face to assist reconstructive surgery following major excision, of a cancer for example. Both of these applications have been pursued successfully by a Japanese professor, Takakazu Maruyasu of Tokyo University. Its assistance in the fitting of dentures is another possibility.

The essence of photogrammetry is the taking of stereo pairs of pictures, usually from different camera positions. Several, even many, pairs of photographs are taken, depending on the size and complexity of the surface; nevertheless, this part of the operation is swift and in no way inconvenient to a patient. Then, when viewed through a binocular microscope, the pictures appear as a three-dimensional model of the surface. They are translated into a map or accurate plot of the features by a complex machine called a photogrammetric plotter, with which the operator scans the stereo-photographs systematically to draw contours uniformly accurate to a thousandth of an inch or better.

Measurement of human skill, and of any impairment that may arise from fatigue or the taking of alcohol or drugs for example, is a complicated matter, because it is compounded of psychological as well as physiological factors. Efforts to provide a scientific basis for legislation on the permissible blood alcohol level for a motorist or pilot well illustrate the point. A British scientist, Dr Martin Wright, writing in the *New Law Journal*, observes that ' ... only under the most exceptional circumstances can driving ability be improved by alcohol. Technically, it will always be impaired, though the impairment may be too small to measure, but it may be argued that under certain circumstances the impairment of a driver's technique may be outweighed by the improvement in his personality. Such circumstances, however, are very hard to define and cannot reasonably be taken account of in legislation.'[10]

An instrument called a stressalyzer has been developed in the laboratories of the National Research Council in Ottawa. It tests human ability in controlling machines and helps to sort out potentially dangerous pilots or drivers, and perhaps politicians or company directors too (see Plate 2). The idea of Dr C. B. Gibbs of the control systems laboratory, it presents a tracking task in which the 'driver' employs a handwheel to align a pointer with one of five tracking target lights, lit briefly in succession. By breaking the sequence occasionally, so that the 'driver' finds he must track in an unexpected direction, it has been found that the normal time it takes for a person to react to the unexpected is four-tenths of a second. Should he react more quickly, the likelihood is that he will make a mistake and choose the wrong direction in which to track. It is a rapid test of the ability to control a machine.

Most men, Dr Gibbs has found, compensate for the effects of stress—from fatigue or intoxication for example—by increasing the time they take to react to the unexpected. But a small minority react more quickly—and in consequence make more errors.

THE HUMAN MECHANISM

A picture begins to emerge of a human mechanism of astonishing versatility, crammed full of sub-systems the control of which is fully automatic, self-regulating and self-repairing. The seat of this versatility is the central nervous system, partly a computer which, although far slower than its electronic counterparts today, kilocycles compared with megacycles a second, has available a 'random access' memory of phenomenal capacity for its size, up to a thousand million 'bits' of information. This astonishingly powerful mechanism, only 2 per cent of the body's weight yet responsible for 18 per cent of its production of heat, is protected from physical abuse by a shell of cranial bone, the body's hardest tissue, that requires a blow of some 300 kilograms to fracture.

Several sensors serve the brain with information. Much the most prolific source is the eye, a camera which, according to Jacobson, can supply up to 4·3 million 'bits' of information a second,[11] 430 times as much as the ear.[12] More sensitive to light than any

39

man-made sensor — it can register the impact of a single photon (or light 'particle'), and performs effectively over a range of illumination greater than 100 million to one — the eye can resolve 100 microns at a range of 10 inches, and distinguish $7\frac{1}{2}$ million different colours. It is, in fact, an extension of the brain itself.

Two further sensors, the nose and the fingertip, can respectively identify any one of 10,000 odours in a single second, and detect a vibration a mere two-hundredths of a micron in amplitude. The skin can detect changes in its temperature of one-thousandth of a degree Centigrade.

Our machine, two-thirds water, runs at the unprecedently low temperature (for a heat engine) of 37° Centigrade (98·6°F). The body's bio-chemistry runs out of control outside quite narrow limits, about 33–41°C. Yet so effective is the body's own thermostat that Eskimos and other races live at temperatures as low as –68°C, while man has survived twenty minutes' exposure to dry still air at 130°C — well above water's boiling point.[13]

This machine requires roughly 10 pounds of fuel a day: 4 pounds apiece of foodstuffs and fluid and 2 pounds of oxygen. No artificial source of power yet conceived can compete for efficiency or convenience. Combusted by enzymes in the process we call digestion, this fuel affords the muscles (roughly half the body's weight) a continuous output of about a quarter of a horsepower. Davies and Rennie found that man can exert very nearly the maximum power output of which his body is capable by bounding vertically into the air in a standing high jump off a force platform.[14] In measurements made on British Navy personnel, they recorded instantaneous power outputs of nearly 7 horsepower for men, and over 3·5 horsepower for women — about fifteen times the output sustained on a bicycle ergometer. An explosive release of energy of this kind is also involved in such activities as the long jump and shot put.

Man's power output has proved sufficient to propel the body at 26·22 miles an hour,[15] or thrust it upwards against the force of gravity to clear $89\frac{3}{4}$ inches. Fed to the levers of the arm, this power has provided a missile delivery system that has hurled a cricket ball at nearly 100 miles an hour, or put the shot for a distance of over 70 feet; and moved the arm (of a Karateka) at more than 30 miles an hour to strike a brick with a force as great as 89 kilograms.[16] Fed to the muscles of the abdomen, it exerts in the female a force approaching one hundredweight in moving a baby along the 4 inches of the birth canal.

This mechanism is immensely adaptable, as we have already seen from the range of temperature that it can tolerate. At very short notice the heart can increase its output of blood five-fold, while the lungs will provide more than ten times the normal demand of oxygen. (It is standard practice among physiologists, in fact, to study the regulation of biological systems by applying a stress and observing how the system adapts.)

Experience with those men who work in the sulphur mines on the summits of extinct volcanoes in Chile indicates that the limit in altitude to which man can permanently adjust is about 17,500 feet; yet 10 million people in the world today live permanently at altitudes as great as 12,000–13,000 feet. As man descends into the sea the air his lungs contain is compressed until, at 100 feet, it occupies only a quarter its original volume. The lungs themselves can diminish no further in volume, and greater depths may cause blood and tissue fluids to be forced into the lungs, and also reverse the transfer of carbon dioxide.

There is often a price to be paid for prolonged exposure to extremes of environment. Everyone is exposed, constantly, to a very low level of ionizing radiation, but any appreciable increase in this level if prolonged can invoke irreversible changes in the cells of the body. Prolonged exposure to pressure, an occupational hazard of divers, can cause marked deterioration in the long bones; while exposure to high levels of noise has a perceptible effect on the acuity of a person's hearing. Man has shown that he can adapt to the gravity-free conditions of space for periods of at least thirty days, but whether this period can be greatly extended is still open to question.

In one Russian experiment, two young men were reported to have spent more than two months lying horizontally in a state of virtual immobility. On the twenty-third day of this experiment their bodies began to ache, and a few days later a third man who had begun with them began to lose orientation in time and space, and was withdrawn. A week later, the report continued, the two remaining volunteers suddenly began to feel much better, their bodies having adjusted to a state of immobility. But when the experiment was through they found they could not stand up, and it was several days before they fully recovered their strength.

What perhaps is even more pertinent is what happens to man when a number of stresses interact on him. We are still sadly short of information about the cumulative effect of stresses upon the human mechanism. To quote a wartime report prepared by submariners in the U.S. Navy submarine *Puffer*, one should 'Be careful and slow to form an estimate of man's value until he has been observed under stress.' The Stressalyzer, which we met earlier, may permit such a measurement, by analysing a man's capacity for taking decisions when his capacity to handle information is approaching its limit. Dr Leslie Buck of the National Research Council has already found a close correlation between an unsatisfactory Stressalyzer performance and the intelligence rating and personality traits of the subject.

MICROMINIATURIZED SYSTEMS

One piece of technology contributes disproportionately towards optimism for the future of man-made biological systems. This is a remarkable device called the integrated circuit; an electronic circuit with the equivalent of tens, hundreds, even thousands of components all engraved within a single chip of material. Although it is only a decade since the integrated circuit was first developed, so rapidly has this microminiature marvel matured that already it offers some persuasive advantages over ordinary electronics, using valves or transistors as the key component.

Credit for the integrated circuit is often given — erroneously as it happens — to the American space programme. Its aetiology can be traced back to the invention of the transistor itself, by the Bell Telephone Laboratories in 1947. Soon after Bell's scientists demonstrated that it was possible to amplify an electric current inside a solid material, by a process of solid-state physics, more far-seeing physicists imagined numbers of similar elements working in concert within the same scrap of material. As early as 1952 a British government scientist, Geoffrey Dummer, published some thoughts for one-piece circuits that 'may consist of layers of insulating, conducting, rectifying and amplifying materials, the electrical functions being connected directly by cutting out areas of the various layers'.

42

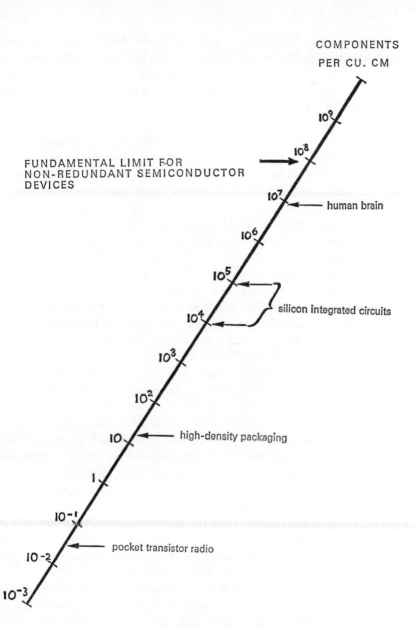

FIG. 6. 'Packing densities' of various microminiature electronic systems

By 1959 one American company, Texas Instruments, backed by a large contract from the U.S. Air Force, was in pilot production with its 'Solid Circuits'. Later—and only later—the U.S. National Aeronautics and Space Administration (NASA) lent its considerable support with decisions, towards the end of 1962, first to use these integrated circuits in the prototype computers for the *Apollo* mooncraft, and then in the Minuteman missile.

I have dwelt on the origins of the integrated circuit because it introduces a technology that promises to become crucially important to the future of bio-medical engineering. It offers four supreme advantages over ordinary electronics: advantages that are particularly relevant to bio-medical engineering. For one thing, it affords an opportunity to make a circuit literally tens of thousands of times smaller. The engineer uses the term 'packing density' to indicate how many components he can squeeze into a given volume, and Fig. 6 shows how integrated circuits compare with the electronics normally found at home and with those of the human brain. As a designer of portable military equipment with microminiature circuits once remarked: 'We're already at the stage of needing soldiers with smaller fingers to adjust the knobs.'

Secondly, the integrated circuit is inherently a far more reliable circuit, with a rate of failure many thousands of times lower than other kinds of circuit; which is why it was chosen for aerospace service. For example, it will survive an acceleration of 20,000 g— roughly that experienced by a well-driven golf ball. There are two reasons for this. One lies in the manufacturing process itself, in which every component is fashioned in a single sequence of operations, from the same piece of material. The other is that the many interconnections, a great source of trouble in ordinary electronics, are an integral part of the circuit. (Unfortunately, one remaining source of weakness, so far as the living body is concerned, are the electrical connections between the circuit, its power supply and the biological mechanism it is controlling.)

A better performance is the third advantage—a direct consequence of the components being packed so close together, for the circuit responds far more quickly, and a more powerful machine becomes possible. The fourth advantage is the inherently low cost of the integrated circuit, once its complicated manufacturing technology has been mastered.

44

The integrated circuit is the key to far more accurate and comprehensive measurements on the living mechanism. What is more, as the subsequent chapters illustrate, the integrated circuit is the *sine qua non* of most of the advanced technology envisaged today. How, then, does it work? Very briefly—for it is a complex piece of physics—the integrated circuit consists of a sliver of silicon, a curious half-metallic element, on which is impressed an intricate pattern. It is possible, by diffusing traces of certain impurities into extremely pure silicon, enormously to vary its ability to conduct electricity. In making an integrated circuit, the engineer builds up, in a long succession of manufacturing steps, a labyrinth of differing electrical conductivities. Each represents a different electrical function, and they are interconnected to produce a complete 'circuit function'.

It sounds simple, although it is anything but. And to quote Professor Wen-Hsiung Ko of the Case Institute of Technology, in a paper to the 1966 National Electronic Conference, 'the implications of this development in circuitry and theory to the natural sciences and life sciences is not fully recognized and cannot be over-emphasized'.[17]

Individually, these circuits are about the size of a pin's head, although when packaged they are normally about as big as a single transistor, for ease of handling. If need be, however, many of these minuscule circuits can be assembled in a single package.

Under the stimulus of aerospace requirements (NASA purchased 200,000 integrated circuits in the first two years for the *Apollo* project alone) the new technology very rapidly reached the consumer market. By the spring of 1964 Fairchild Semiconductor was offering the circuits at commercially attractive prices; and Zenith Radio Corporation had collaborated with another circuit maker, Texas Instruments, to develop an amplifier for a hearing aid using an integrated circuit containing six transistors and sixteen resistors.

At the other end of the scale, however, is a technique called 'large scale integration', now on the verge of making circuits with thousands and even tens of thousands of components. We shall meet such a circuit later, in the form of an experimental television camera.

Perhaps the most exciting consequence of large-scale integration

45

will be the self-repairing computer. Large-scale integration itself will improve the reliability of complex circuitry by orders of magnitude, but it will also allow the circuit designer to duplicate or triplicate his components and sub-systems at no great extra cost. The spare parts could then be called into play by means of a built-in diagnostic logic circuit and the appropriate computer programme, which would locate the fault and effect a self-repair. As Earl C. Joseph told a computer congress in Edinburgh in 1968, 'Such a self-healing computer system, using electronic surgery, need only be maintained manually when its spare parts became exhausted.'

The immense significance of the integrated circuit permeates every section of this book, in the contribution it can make towards measuring, amplifying and even mimicking man's natural functions. The integrated circuit is beginning to allow the physiologist and the engineer to penetrate the living body in a way that would otherwise be impossible, or would so distort the situation as to be meaningless. The 'radio pill' is one of the most remarkable examples of an electronic system for taking measurements deep within the body, without interrupting or in any way affecting its normal performance, as we shall see a little later.

The smallness and reliability of the circuit and its modest power requirements make it no less attractive, when 'potted' in a suitable plastic, for surgical implantation. In this form it can be used to drive pacemakers and other electronic controls, and in the future to perform much more complicated functions in controlling the body's organs. The same considerations apply to external prostheses like artificial limbs or sensory aids for the blind or deaf.

Then there is a third function, no less promising, in the monitoring of patients, where a very complicated sequence of measurements and checks can be made, entirely automatically and repetitively, by equipment that remains small and inexpensive enough to mount at the bedside. Such a system of 'intensive care' will call human attention to the patient as soon as one of the measurements—temperature, blood pressure, respiration, electrocardiogram (E.C.G.), electroencephalogram (E.E.G.), and so forth—moves outside preset limits.

The technology of the integrated circuit is still developing very rapidly. Not only is there every possibility of packing still more components into a given volume, but also of devising new and more versatile components. For example, it has recently become possible to build a source of microwaves into an integrated circuit (see Plate 3) and to construct a circuit that is itself capable of amplifying and measuring pressures—inside a blood vessel, for example.

But there are parts of an electrical circuit that are still very difficult to microminiaturize, and one of the most important of these is the power supply. Even integrated circuits normally need several volts, and consume appreciable amounts of energy in order to drive their appropriate output, such as a transmitter or pacemaker or hearing aid; no easy matter when one considers that ideally they should run for years at a stretch.

At present these 'active' devices, including those actually implanted in the body, are battery driven, powered by a modern version of the familiar 'dry' torch battery. This is the mercury battery, with about five times the storage capacity of the usual torch battery and, no less important, the ability to maintain its output almost unchanged until very near the end of its life. This is the battery that drives an electric watch, normally for about a year without attention.

Mercury batteries used for implanted heart pacemakers are manufactured to especially high standards of reliability. 'Certified cells', as they are known, are made to serve continuously at body temperature under an average current drain of 20 millionths of an ampere. Each is the size of a small button and five or six provide the eight volts needed by an implantable pacemaker.

The cardiac pacemaker, described later, is usually implanted in an accessible place in the anterior abdominal wall. At the present stage of its development the battery is not the weakest point; this tends to be the leads and electrodes that couple its current to the ever-moving tissues, which are being constantly flexed and fail from fatigue. Nevertheless, the battery needs to be replaced at intervals from a few months to two or three years—one survey of cardiac pacemakers has put the mean survival time at only sixteen months. More lasting sources of power are under development, including nuclear powerpacks with a ten-year life.

Nothing has served more dramatically to bring the consequences of microminiaturized electronics to the attention of a large public than contemporary interest in espionage, where engineering marvels like the 'bugged' cocktail olive that will transmit a conversation to another room are already a wholly accepted part of the folklore. But if the value of the electronic 'bug' in espionage has perhaps been overrated, this can hardly be said of its value in physiology, where it offers the prospect of relaying information from the farthermost recesses of a body without the slightest inconvenience to its owner. Professor Stuart Mackay, one of the pioneers in the development of 'endoradiosondes', as once they were named, used to swallow one before a lecture, so that his audience might follow the pressure changes in his alimentary tract on a screen.

Radio pills, as these miniature transmitters are often known today, have two main functions: to sense something (pressure or temperature, pH or the presence of blood, for example), and to transmit what they sense on a radio wave. Living tissues are transparent to radio waves to a depth of one-tenth to one-hundredth of their wavelength.[18] The variable under observation is arranged to modulate the frequency of the transmitted signal, so that it follows the pattern of the changes. This signal can then be picked up by quite simple radio receiving equipment outside the body.

Pressure, for example, can be arranged to act through a small diaphragm in the radio pill, thereby changing the characteristics of the transmitter within, and thus its frequency of transmission. Temperature changes can be sensed by a special electrical device called a 'thermistor', or thermally sensitive resistor, a scrap of semi-conducting material whose electrical impedance changes with its temperature. The acidity (pH value) of, say, the stomach can be sensed by a tiny glass electrode built into the radio pill.

Usually the power supply driving the radio pill is sealed into the device—Mallory makes a mercury cell less than a centimetre across for the purpose. This will often power the radio pill for some days, and much longer if arranged to transmit only intermittently, so the device if carefully sealed can be buried deep within the tissues for weeks at a stretch. On the other hand, if taken into the alimentary tract by way of the mouth, the radio pill will normally be expelled within forty-eight hours.

Wen-Hsiung Ko of the Case Institute of Technology in Cleveland, Ohio, has suggested a further experimental refinement in

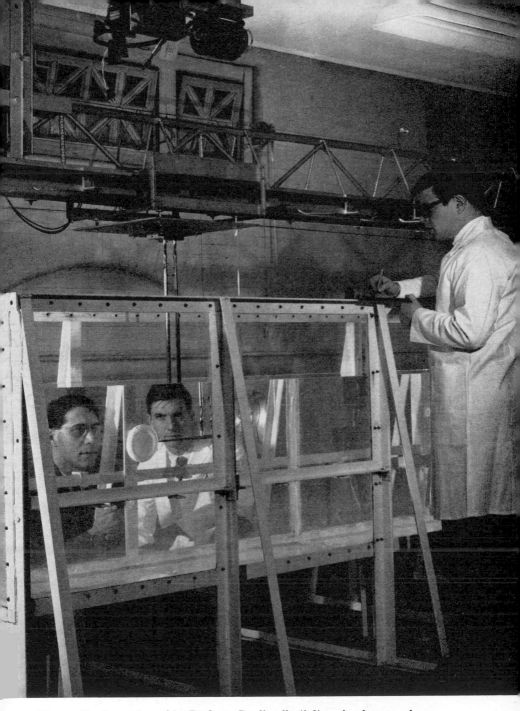

Plate I. Towing tank used by Professor Bugliarello (*left*) to simulate on a large scale conditions encountered by the red blood cells in passing through capillaries. A model of a red blood cell can be seen in the tank.

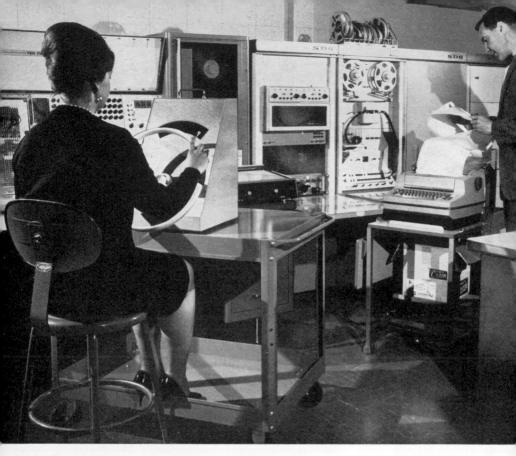

Plate 2. Stressalyzer, developed by Canada's National Research Council to measure stress and analyse a person's capacity to control a machine

Plate 3. Microminiature radar including transmitter, receiver and aerial

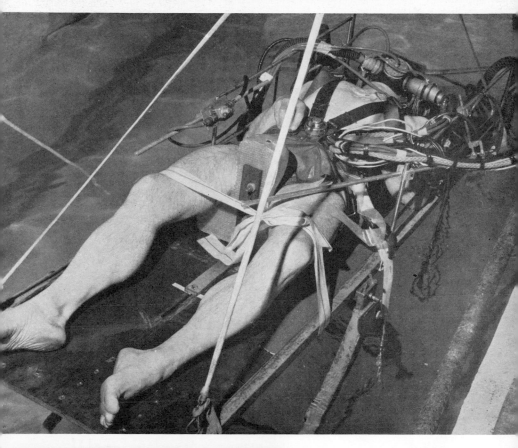

Plate 4. Instrumented subject, festooned with connections, awaiting immersion in salt water at the R.A.F. Institute of Aviation Medicine at Farnborough. It illustrates the difficulties encountered in taking many physiological measurements simultaneously

Plate 5. Implantable 'passive' radio pills, developed to measure fluid pressures within the eyeball

Plate 6. Control of this rocket propuls
system is an excellent example of a v
complex man-machine interaction

Plate 7. Handyman, General Electr
hydro-mechanical master-slave manip
tor, operated by its designer, Ralph Mos

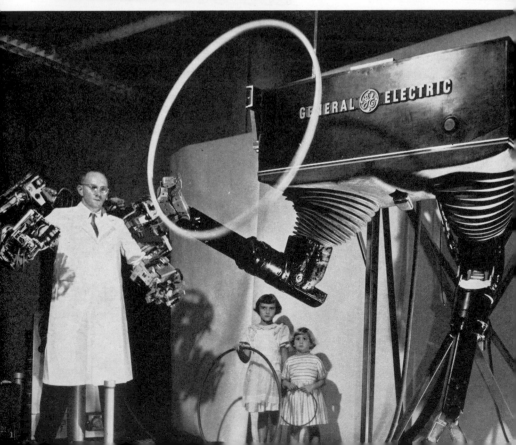

which a radio transmitter is combined with electrical stimulation of the kind a pacemaker can provide, in order to compare a particular response with the stimulation that has been administered.

Many useful measurements can be made on the living body without entering it at all, of course, but to make them continuously the patient may have to be festooned with wires and connections, as in Plate 4. This may be highly inconvenient even for a captive patient, and would normally be out of the question for a fit person. Yet there is much still to be learned about the performance and behaviour of the person who is perfectly well and simply going about his everyday activities. This curiosity about the norm, which could provide clues to the origins of many diseases, has led the bio-engineering laboratory of the National Institute for Medical Research in London to apply microminiaturization to the development of a family of 'socially acceptable monitoring instruments' or SAMIS.

The SAMI, conceived by Heinz Wolff, head of the laboratory, is a device convenient enough to study the human being in his natural environment: a miniature recorder, at its present stage of development about the size of a packet of twenty cigarettes, and weighing one and a half ounces, that will log a physiological factor such as a heart rate. SAMIS were worn by some of the drivers in a motor rally in England in November 1966, using electrodes stuck to their chests with a sticky jelly to pick up the electrical signals generated by each heart-beat (E.C.G.). Signals are stored in a small electrochemical cell, in effect a battery that works in reverse, depositing silver in proportion to the current flowing. It can then be 'replayed' in the laboratory to give a continuous E.C.G. The research workers were surprised to find their drivers sustained the high pulse rate of 100–110 whilst driving, although such a rate is normally associated only with a man doing strenuous exercise, a coal miner for example.

Variants of the SAMI are planned to allow investigations of many groups of people who, so far as they are aware, are perfectly fit and free-roaming — children, housewives, executives, for example — to try to relate changes in heart rate, temperature and other factors to their activities and changes of environment. Broadly speaking there is a need for two kinds of monitor: one that

D

registers, say, the number of heart-beats over a longish period, a day or week, perhaps; and one that plots the variable against time, to show up the effects of severe exercise, emotional stress, sleep or other changes.

Still smaller is the E.C.G. transmitter developed by Lawrence Kavanagh of the Royal College of Surgeons, for implantation near the heart, which can be switched on and off by bringing a magnet near a tiny switch buried beneath the skin. It is designed around an integrated circuit and includes a microminiature crystal that keeps its frequency of transmission within the very narrow waveband, 102·36–102·39 MHz, allotted by the British Post Office for medical telemetry.

The biological benefits of microminiaturization are not derived solely from electronics. There is, for example, the work of Carter Collins of the Institute of Medical Services at the Presbyterian Medical Center in San Francisco, who has developed a pressure sensor small enough to be buried in a brain, an artery or even an eye.[19] There have been many attempts to measure the pressures exerted by body fluids in small vessels, using radio pills, but none has proved small enough, at least for the living eye. Dr Collins set out to make a sensor an order of magnitude smaller than the battery-driven pills.

His sensor actually works in reverse. Instead of broadcasting the pressures it detects, it responds to those pressures by absorbing energy from radio waves. In fact, it is simply a tiny aerial: two wispy coils that absorb radio waves of a certain frequency, depending on how close together the pressure has pushed them. A wide-band oscillator provides the radio signal, the frequency of which is swept over the required waveband to find the frequency at which the coils are resonating and so absorbing energy.

Dr Collins's detector or 'transensor', need be no bigger than a pinhead (see Plate 5) with coils only half a millimetre across, and can be surgically implanted for months at a stretch. It encapsulates a small bubble of air, as little as 0·003 millilitre, to which the pressure changes are transmitted through a thin plastic diaphragm. In this way he has measured a (relatively enormous) pressure rise of more than 70 millimetres of mercury in a rabbit's eye when the rabbit blinked, and changes of intracranial pressure of a few centimetres of water. He also finds that the pressure rises when other senses are stimulated — which may be why male eyes tend to pop when they glimpse a glamorous girl.

Yet we need far more precise and detailed measurements of the performance of every sub-system in the human machine for the pursuit of almost all the technology discussed in the chapters that follow. Just as the computer is forcing the surgeon to replace observations like 'he's just a bit cyanosed' with a precise measurement of his patient's blood oxygen level, so the engineer's ambition to amplify, augment, even mimic the living mechanism calls for accurate data obtained from the body, not when ailing, but at the peak of its performance. Only a microminiaturized system, so designed that it can glean data unperceived by the human guinea pig it is measuring, will provide it.

CHAPTER TWO

Man Amplified

'In dealing with the human operator we are dealing with the blackest of "black boxes".'

Professor Tom Sheridan

So FAR, my chief concern has been to develop the picture of man the machine: a marvellous mechanism, still so little understood, particularly so far as the processes of 'feedback', control and self-correction (*homeostasis*), reasoning and creativity are concerned. Man, nevertheless, is sadly deficient in many specific respects in his physical performance—weak, fragile, slow of movement compared with other animals, easily fatigued, vulnerable to comparatively small changes of temperature and pressure, to noise and many kinds of radiation. Since early man first provided himself with a cave as shelter from the elements and from intruders he has sought constantly to improve his physical capacity (see Fig. 7).

The most obvious way in which he has done so is in providing himself with a tougher sheath than hair and skin alone can afford. Thus, early man shielded himself from the vagaries of the weather and to some extent from scratches and bruises occasioned by hunting. Later he used the same materials to fashion shields and tunics that would help protect him in battle. As weapons became more dangerous, they gave way to primitive armour, and eventually to the elaboration of chain mail.

But the striking power of weapons improved more rapidly than the technology of armour, and the warrior soon found that adequate protection meant virtual immobility, for the individual

52

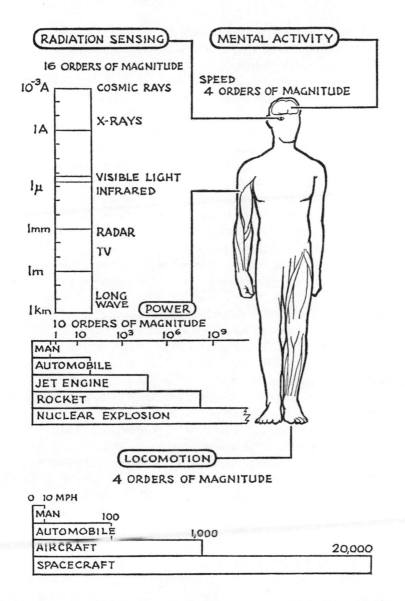

FIG. 7. Man amplified: how man's faculties compare with modern machines and sensors

soldier at least. Except for the helmet, armour was discarded for several centuries, until very recent times. Then studies on wounds received during the Second World War and the war in Korea showed that the great majority of fatalities were due to wounds of the chest or abdomen, which contain the major organs other than the brain. Just a square foot of armour, front and back of the torso, might have prevented two-thirds of them. New developments in materials are making possible 'vests' that are proof not merely against revolver bullets, but against the armour-piercing projectiles of modern warfare.

Man requires protection in many activities other than warfare: in industrial environments, where excesses of heat and cold, corrosive or toxic chemicals, or high levels of noise, dust or radiation may prevail; in medical practice, where infection is often a hazard; even in recreation, where helmets, boots, gloves, pads, and so on, and sometimes entire suits, are concomitants of many sporting activities.

But no environment is more hostile than space; no activity calls for a more sophisticated suit than spaceflight. The suit developed for Major Edward White's 'walk' in space in 1965 not only furnished the astronaut with oxygen at a rate that remained under his control, but also provided protection against radiation and micrometeoroids, against excessive heat and cold, and against the sun's glare. Yet it was supple enough to allow a considerable freedom of movement, and for it to be donned and removed again within the confines of the spacecraft.

Spaceflight is a highly specialized activity, of course, but the principles of totally protecting an individual against a hostile environment apply elsewhere—even within the factory. A few years ago the U.S. Bureau of Naval Weapons sponsored the construction of a metal-working plant at the Universal Cyclops Company that operated in an atmosphere of very pure argon. The plant, contained within a room about 100 feet long and over 20 feet high, dealt with metals like molybdenum, which when very hot are readily attacked by atmospheric oxygen. Operators wore space suits fed with air, and entered the plant by way of air locks. The approach was successful but costly— $1,000 a day to run—and cheaper techniques eventually supplanted the argon atmosphere. But the same principles have since found application in the

54

Anaerobic Laboratory of the National Institutes of Health, near Washington, where such diseases as tetanus, the bacteria of which thrive when oxygen is absent, are being studied.

Many men have a psychological need to engage in activities that involve some element of personal danger, while many more gain considerable vicarious satisfaction from such exploits. There is little doubt that space activity would arouse not a fraction of the interest it does were men not intimately involved. The fire that asphyxiated three astronauts on the launch-pad in a faulty *Apollo* spacecraft early in 1967 engendered far more interest than the quite fantastic technological achievements of sending the unmanned *Mariner V* 134 million miles to Mars, or soft-landing the satellite *Venera IV* on the surface of Venus. As we shall see, however, there are still more compelling reasons for having a man at the controls.

But first let us take that most ubiquitous of tasks among industrialized nations today, the repetitive operation on the production line. Here the principal hazard would appear to be boredom. Viewed as an assembly mechanism 'the human machine is a masterpiece of versatility and sensing capability', a conference of engineers in Nottingham, in 1967, was told by Eric Desmond of Smiths Industries. But it 'has weaknesses as well as virtues. It is unpredictable, unreliable, and inconsistent. It varies in ability, fatigues easily, has to sleep and be refuelled at regular intervals, goes on strike, works to rule, and needs holidays every year.'

Formidable handicaps, you may think. Yet manufacturers in the mass-production industries continue to pay about two-thirds of their wage bill to assembly-line workers. (One American furniture manufacturer tried chimps on his production line, stuffing upholstery, but the idea did not catch on.)

The fact remains that, just as one of the more commonplace robots about the home today, the washing-up machine, is none too good at the awkward jobs like shifting the last traces of congealed egg, so the industrial robot has its limitations. After quite a few years of attempting to build machines that would supplant the human assembly-line worker, the production engineer is becoming convinced that his first task is usually to redesign his product, eradicating as far as possible the thousand and one trivial adjustments that even the most unintelligent assembly worker

55

needs to make, mostly quite unconsciously, in the course of assembling an assortment of parts. But once done, a man-machine partnership may still be the more economic route.

To further amplify his physical processes man has made another kind of robot, more versatile than the mechanisms built into assembly machines. This kind has a 'brain' of sorts, or rather a memory, that can be trained—'programmed'—to carry through a lengthy sequence of operations. One American machine, a one-armed robot, simulates waist, shoulder, elbow, wrist and finger movements, and can be trained to remember as many as 200 separate movements and recall them in the right sequence. Its 'fingers' will grasp parts up to 75 pounds in weight and move them to any position, at any angle, within a volume of 350 cubic feet. Yet so dainty are its movements that it makes an excellent job of pouring a cup of tea. 'Unimate', as this robot is called, is designed to work for 40,000 hours, a figure worth comparing with the performance of its human counterpart, which rarely works for the same employer for more than about 2,000 hours a year.

Unimate (and similar machines) have been conceived for a very great diversity of industrial roles, and today can be found assembling parts, handling glass or hot metal, generally engaged in a host of activities that tend to denigrate the dignity of human labour. More specific versions will no doubt follow, that exchange precision for versatility, or which are possessed of a sensory capacity, a perception that would recognize, say, an incorrect part or orientation, or a hazardous operating situation. A British professor, Meredith Thring, believes such robots have a place in the home, cleaning, laying tables or making the beds, for example; though I feel there may be a psychological flaw here, in that the 'black box' should be as inconspicuous as possible if man is not to find its presence abhorrent, as might well be the case with a robot 'housemaid' scurrying around the home.

Apart from machines that serve in the production line or the home there is also a rather special kind of robot, the intrepid machine that ventures where man would fear to tread, not so much to do a job but to garner information. It may sit in an automobile that is about to be crash-tested, to measure the forces imposed upon the occupant of the driving seat; or be tossed from an aircraft to try out a new parachute or ejection seat; or squat

56

for months on end in a nuclear shelter, the sweaty fate of the 'simocs', or simulated occupants. Such a robot is usually called a phantom.

A space suit pressurized to four or five pounds severely cramps the movements of its wearer, but by just how much the wearer can only estimate. NASA's Manned Spaceflight Center, needing more precise information, commissioned the Illinois Institute of Technology Research Institute in Chicago to construct a phantom that would simulate human motions. The outcome was a very sophisticated force gauge, hydraulically powered and remotely controlled, resembling a human being in shape and size and in the way it moves its thirty-five joints, thirty-three of them fitted with strain-gauge torque sensors. In fact, it does almost everything but walk (which would also require a sense of balance, of course).

These phantoms—two were constructed—were adjustable in all vital statistics, to embrace all but the smallest and largest five percentages of the population. But their creators met a snag in seeking reliable figures for the strengths of the various human joints, for frequently medical data conflicted or could not be found at all. For several joints they used measurements made on their own staff.

A few years ago British scientists analysed the design of a very popular make of metal-working lathe, to see what shape of person might be best equipped to operate it. They came to the conclusion that it had been designed for use by the broad-shouldered dwarf sketched in Fig. 8.

This is no isolated example. The idea of designing a machine—any machine—to take full account of the advantages and limitations of the 'human factor', its psychology as well as its physiology, is a comparatively new one. That is not to say, however, that most machines are badly designed—quite the reverse, in fact, for machines that have been around a long time tend to have become more and more closely adapted to the human factor. The bicycle and the motor car are good examples, although a strong case can still be made for a detailed analysis of the car, on the grounds that either safety or ease of driving, or probably both, will be improved. (The cynical view here of course is that, whatever the outcome, it will not sell more cars.)

Whereas the car has steadily become simpler to drive, other

57

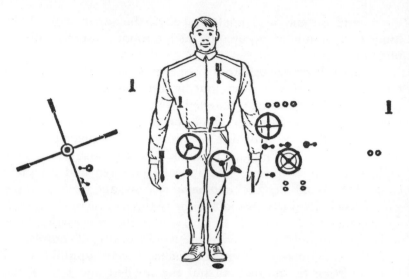

FIG. 8. Ideal shape for the operator for one well-known make of capstan lathe, reached on the basis of ergonomic studies

machines, especially military machines, have grown enormously more complicated since the Second World War, and the successful use of such a system as a modern fighter or early-warning radar, or the man-propelling rocket system shown in Plate 6, now depends crucially on the intimacy with which man and machine can interact. The late Dr Paul Fitts, a leading figure in the world of human-factors engineering, in a report prepared by a panel he headed for the U.S. military in 1953, summarized the point adroitly when he said: 'A new weapon that can be operated only by a man with three arms is not engineered for human use, nor is a system to be relied upon in battle if it is so complex that only the scientists who designed it can maintain it in operation.'

Nowadays, the weapon may be worth 2 million pounds in the case of a single-seat, high-performance aircraft; 50 million pounds in the case of a missile-carrying nuclear submarine.

'Mismatch' between man and the machines he uses occurs far more commonly than is normally realized, and is one of the commonest sources of inefficiency and error. Mismatch arises in the home, for instance with the telephone, where some numbers have proved difficult to memorize accurately; and on the road, where all too frequently man finds himself unable to retain full control of his car (in Europe road accidents are the leading cause of death up to the age of forty-five). It arises in the factory, with machines like the lathe in Fig. 8, and in the skies with instruments (altimeters for example) that can easily be misread. Indeed, so far as the car is concerned it has been argued that, so great is the mismatch, the vehicle should be designed on the assumption that eventually it will crash, with far more attention being paid to the survival of the occupants.[1]

One might therefore conclude that, rather than attempt to adapt the machine to man's limitations, it would be simpler to eliminate the 'human error' by designing man out altogether. Although superficially attractive, this argument ignores the advantages of that most 'adaptive' of all machines—man—and more particularly the value of man in taking ultimate decisions. As a psychologist once put it to me, 'We can't yet give a machine the instinct to survive.' Rather, the approach that is being developed

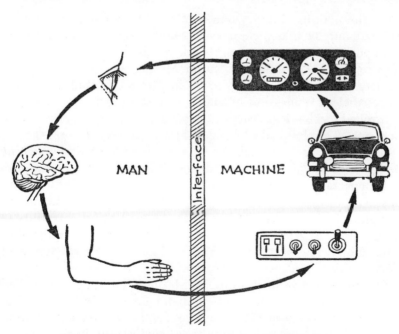

FIG. 9. The man-machine concept, central to human factors techniques today

today is to make the fullest use of man as a superb system of sensory faculties, with the machine watching for any sign that the living system is fatigued or overloaded.

The human factor, then, is the province of the applied psychologist. In the U.S.A. the technology is usually known as human-factors engineering; in Britain as ergonomics. The difference, if there is one, is that human factors tend to place less emphasis on physiology and more on psychology than ergonomics does. It leads us to the conceptual model of man-machine symbiosis sketched in Fig. 9, and described by its authors, T. B. Sheridan and W. R. Ferrell of the Massachusetts Institute of Technology, in these terms: 'We consider a man-machine system to be an assemblage of people and machines which are in significant communication with one another and which are performing a task sufficiently well defined that independent and dependent variables and criteria of performance may be operationally specified.'[2]

AMPLIFYING THE PHYSICAL PROCESSES

That the man-machine system is often poorly designed has been pointed out by many engineers. 'Man's capability for intricate manipulating and controlling is not readily appreciated because it is so familiar,' remarked Ralph Mosher at a meeting of the Society of Automotive Engineers in Detroit in January 1967. 'Nevertheless, separation of man and task by a lever- or pedal-controlled mechanical system causes a degradation of performance in terms of mechanical filtering of human sense.'

Mosher, a project engineer in control systems and machine design at General Electric's Advanced Technology Laboratories in Schenectady, is trying to put back what the machine filters out. His CAMS, or cybernetic anthropomorphous machines, unite man's complex of sensory mechanisms with the power and versatility of a machine, a symbiosis with possibilities that are altogether astonishing. The sketches of Fig. 10 illustrate several stages of sophistication in attaining true symbiosis.

One of the machines built in Mosher's laboratory is called Handyman, a master-slave manipulator for working with radio-active substances (see Plate 7). Man's vulnerability to radiation is a serious handicap in a world that is making rapidly growing use of radioactivity, and some highly ingenious engineering has

Method	Cortical command	Body actuation	Control advantage
Master-slave movement	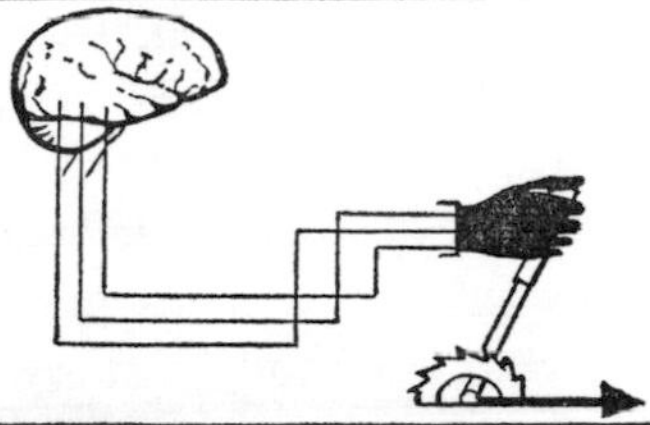		Positioning by direct mechanical coupling
Trip switches sequentially to control powered actuators	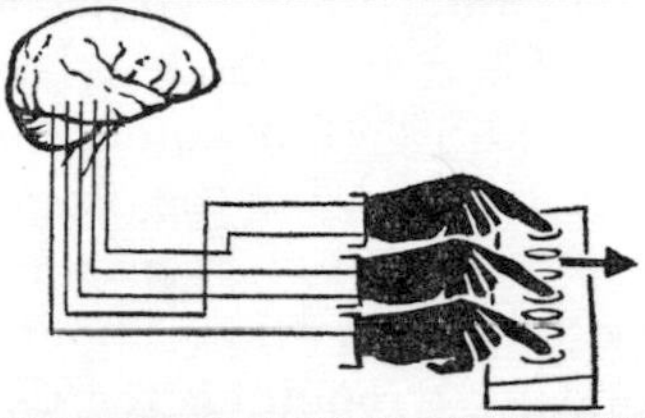		Simple choice based on visual feedback
Trip switches to turn on sequencing program for powered actuators			Programmed actuation — reduces task attention needed
Control signals tapped from muscle (EMG) activity	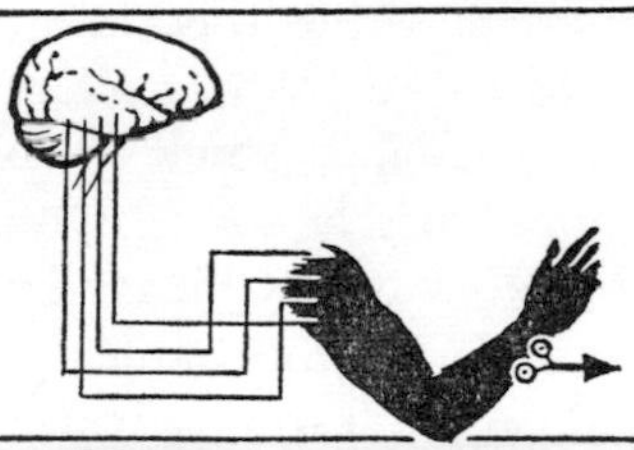		Faster response, and automatic responses can be harnessed. Possibility of using kinesthetic (feel) feedback
Control signals tapped direct from brain			Operation and control by intention

FIG. 10. Steps in the evolution of the human command-control link (after *International Science and Technology*)

developed in consequence. When working with Handyman, the operator remains on one side of a thick concrete wall, his sole connection with the machine an electrical one. Yet beyond the wall the machine mimics its master's arm, finger and thumb movements with such finesse that it can twirl a hula-hoop with its one digit. The man-machine coupling, contends Mosher, is so direct and detailed that the man need not think about the machine at all; he simply concentrates on the task.[3]

Handyman illustrates the solution to another problem. One overriding weakness of robots of the kind we met earlier in this chapter is that they don't know their own strength. Even so simple a task as the opening of a door, which a child normally learns before the age of two, requires a fair amount of effort on the part of the central nervous system, sensing the progress being made and adjusting continually to the changing circumstances. The robot, lacking any feedback of information about the progress it is making, would respond by wrenching the door from its hinges. The problem, then, is to build into the machine a sensitivity to changes of force and position; a 'kinesthetic' sense, as it is called, that can be relayed swiftly and accurately to its operator, and acted upon.

In the case of Handyman and its offspring in the General Electric stable, this kinesthetic sense is supplied by hydraulic servo-mechanisms that are sensitive to position, velocity and force; what the engineer would call a hydromechanical force-feedback system, in which small mechanical movements are transformed into fluid pressures, and back again. Raymond Goertz at the Argonne National Laboratory near Chicago has demonstrated the same principles with an electro-mechanical system, in a manipulator that is adaptable enough to repair itself if it should break down.

The CAMS, by and large, attempt to simulate the action of the arm: of shoulder, elbow, wrist and, to a limited extent only, the fingers. A Japanese research team has approached the matter from the other end. What makes man so skilful is the versatility of his hands, which permits him to grasp and manipulate tools. Professor Masahiro Mori and his colleagues at the Institute of Industrial Science in Tokyo University are developing artificial fingers that can be programmed through a computer to carry out quite complicated tasks—perhaps even to use chopsticks, I was told.

When I visited this laboratory in 1967, Mori was constructing his second set of fingers, three 'fingers' and a 'thumb', controlled by two 'eyes' (TV cameras operating through a pattern-recognizing system), with two sensory devices on each finger to provide kinesthetic feedback. Behind its design lay a detailed theoretical analysis of the hand's function, achieved with the help of a survey carried out by another Japanese scientist, Dr H. Natori, nearly half a century ago.

Dr Natori was then concerned to establish the role of the hand in different kinds of work, and he gathered data from the distribution of callosities on the hands of craftsmen in some 200 different crafts in the Kyoto district, an area famous for the quality of its handicraft. It transpired that nearly 60 per cent of the work done by the hand requires the fingers alone, and co-operation between finger or thumb and palm accounts for a further 30 per cent. Mori's team went on to establish that the most important single action of the hand is the pinch of finger and thumb—the action usually simulated by robots and by prosthetic hands, as we shall see in the next chapter—and to rate the fingers in order of importance: thumb, index finger, second finger, ring finger and little finger. (So relatively unimportant is the little finger that they have left it out of their current model.)

In the effort to amplify man's capabilities, a number of very sophisticated pieces of machinery have been developed that exploit the man-machine (sometimes called the 'master-slave') relationship at a considerable distance. This is a technology for which Dr John W. Clark of the Battelle Memorial Institute has coined the term 'telechirics', from two Greek words, *tele* meaning 'distant' and *kheir* or *chir* meaning 'hand'.

The ultimate objective is a sensitive coupling of the operator's nervous system to powered manipulators that may be not merely stronger but altogether more versatile than human limbs, to permit him to work within a hostile environment without actually entering it. The most important point about a telechiric system is that it is not simply a robot, with a programmed set of responses, but a true integration of man and machine, that can adapt to the situations it encounters.

One technology that has shown considerable interest in telechirics is nuclear energy, and a number of curious machines have been developed to assist in the event of a nuclear accident. One is the 'mobile remote manipulator unit' built by the F.M.C. Corporation for the U.S. Air Force Weapons Laboratory. This is a radio-controlled version of an Army XM147 cargo carrier: an 11-ton monster with 2 manipulators, each having 6 degrees of freedom and a 19-foot reach. Three television cameras (one stereoscopic) are the 'eyes' of this 20-foot machine, which can be driven at up to 10 miles an hour from its near-by control caravan. The vehicle was developed during a U.S. Air Force programme involving the study and development of a global system for crash rescues and salvage operations involving nuclear-powered apparatus.

A smaller telechiric machine that features a high degree of mobility has been designed by H. A. Ballinger, at Harwell, the U.K. Atomic Energy Research Establishment. It assumes considerable difficulties of access in the event of a nuclear incident. RIVET, the 'remote inspection vehicle' (see Plate 8), moves with the profile of a crawling man to gain access, but once in position can stand erect in order to deploy its 'eyes' and 'arms'. The one-third size model of this tank-like vehicle, only 500 pounds in weight and 30 inches in height (unfolding to 6 feet when erect) can run up and down stairs at 45 degrees, surmount a steep obstacle of its own height (a desk for example), right itself if turned upside down, and disentangle itself from an obstruction lodged beneath its belly. Its role would be to visit the scene of a nuclear incident involving high radiation levels, and report the extent of the damage.

It was a nuclear incident that drew the world's attention to the Spanish port of Palomares early in 1966, after a disabled U.S. Air Force bomber had jettisoned a hydrogen bomb into the Mediterranean Sea. In this case, however, the environment, although most decidedly hostile, did not include a lot of radioactivity. What it did provide was first-hand experience of the immense difficulties to be encountered in working on the sea floor.

The problem was first to locate the bomb on the steep and rugged sea bed, and then to raise it. Two deep-diving submersibles took part, *Alvin*, a research vehicle 22 feet in length with a three-man crew and a single arm that protrudes from her nose; and

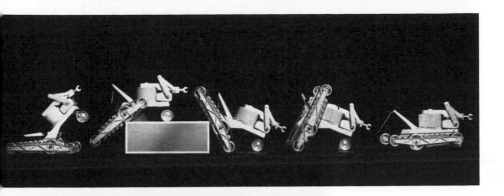

Plate 8. Working model of RIVET, a remote inspection vehicle that could navigate a disaster zone, then hoist itself erect to work

Plate 9. Experiments with an 'exo-skeleton' in General Electric's Research and Development Center

Plate 10. Pedipulator, a
18-foot balancin
machine built by Gener
Electric engineers, th
balance of which can b
controlled by the natur
balance motions of i
operator

Plate 11. At the touch of a button this display of a complex propeller blade, drawn electronically from numerical data stored in a computer, can be set to rotate, revealing every facet

Plate 12. Sim 1, a computer-controlled medical teaching aid developed for the University of Southern California School of Medicine

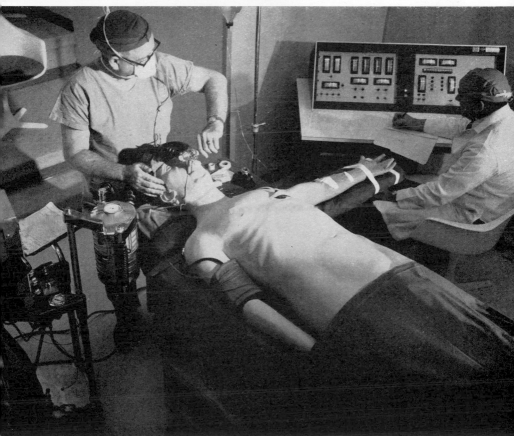

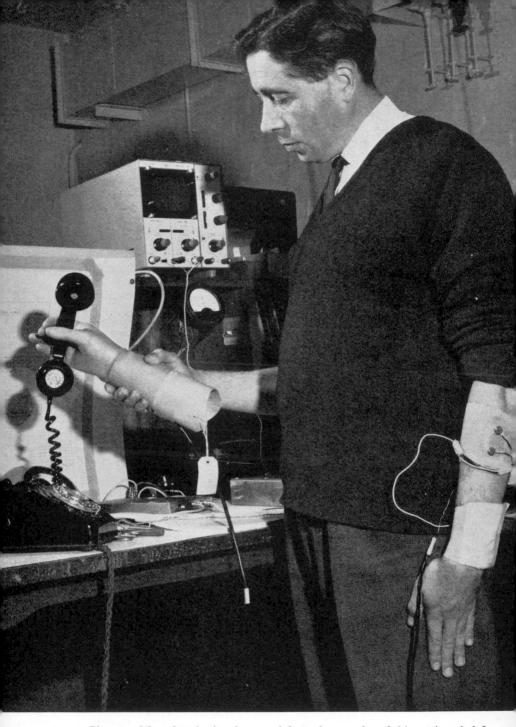

Plate 13. Myo-electric signals tapped from the muscles of this engineer's left forearm are controlling the artificial hand he is holding

Aluminaut, a 50-foot submarine. *Alvin* found the bomb, 2,500 feet deep, and still with its voluminous parachute attached, which she grasped and spread out on the sea bed. But the first attempt at raising the weapon failed when the lifting line broke and the bomb tumbled several hundred feet down a slope. Located once more, the aquanauts this time brought into action a military device called CURV, a cable-controlled underwater recovery vehicle, designed by the Naval Ordnance Test Station at Pasadena specifically to recover test-weapons like torpedoes from the ocean. CURV, which could 'swim' freely in any direction, was operated from a surface ship.

According to one official report,[4] 'some of the tensest moments of the entire search were now experienced by Wilson and McCamis, who were at *Alvin*'s controls. The strain on the parachute shrouds had stirred up the bottom silt considerably, reducing visibility from about twenty-five or thirty feet, to which the pilots had become accustomed at that depth, to about zero. Cautiously, they edged into the cloud of silt, peering intently into the reflected glare of the spotlight beam. Suddenly, immediately in front of them, they confronted the parachute, part of which billowed above the ocean floor like a circus tent and part of which, apparently, had rolled up around the bomb, encasing it like a mummy. Realizing that if *Alvin* became enfolded in the parachute they would probably be unable to free themselves, the pilots turned sharply away, relying on the vehicle's quick response to its controls to avoid entrapment. The parachute did entangle itself in CURV, but not seriously enough to hamper the lifting operation, which was then begun.'

Submersible telechirics, however, will probably offer a more versatile approach for the future, in an environment that man is bound to find arduous and hazardous.

Much more accessible than space, and potentially more profitable, the oceans—and particularly that relatively shallow strip around the coastline known as the continental shelf—are beginning to attract the interest and sponsorship of both governments and private industry. One important objective is to develop the techniques that will allow man himself to work at depths of at least 600 feet, and preferably at 1,000 feet. These include the prospect, no longer remote as we shall see, of artificial gills.

The primary limitation on the activities of a telechiric system is likely to be the cable, its 'umbilical cord'; and even this could probably be dispensed with if need be.

One of the earliest telechiric systems, Shell's 'swimming socket wrench', was designed to work on the sea bed, completing the assembly of underwater oil well-heads. This is the Mobot, first developed around 1962 by Hughes Aircraft Corporation for Shell, and equipped in its latest form not only to turn screws but to 'see' (television), 'hear' (sonar), turn valves and wire-brush a surface (to remove fouling) at a depth of 1,000 feet. Still more ingenious is UNUMO, the universal underwater mobot, another Hughes development, with four arms — two for work and two for hanging on to the well-head.

A submersible telechiric system is not a simple machine. The turbulent medium in which it must perform creates considerable difficulties for the designer of a sufficiently stable platform from which complex manoeuvres might be contemplated. Some of the problems were discussed at a conference on the 'Technology of the sea and seabed', held at Harwell in April 1967, when H. A. Ballinger advanced his ideas for a multi-purpose telechiric capable of such tasks as systematic rock-sampling over a large area, inspection of wrecks, terrain, and so on, and undersea rescue operations.

The Sextapus, as Ballinger calls his six-limbed telechiric, has four powerful suction pads on telescopic legs with which to anchor itself, and a pair of manipulators with which to work. Its operator (and co-pilot, if needed for a difficult job) would sit in a control cabin aboard a surface ship, insulated as far as possible from any distractions unrelated to the Sextapus itself. The command link with the craft would take the form of two 'master arms' with the shoulder pivot joints just above the pilot's own shoulders, and a one-to-one ratio of movement. Gross movements of the manipulators would be made by push-button control, but for manipulative movements a servo-mechanism would link the master-slave motions.

Unfortunately, a kinesthetic sense imparted by force-feedback, as is used for instance in Handyman, would not be possible in this environment because of the large hydro-dynamic forces acting on the manipulators. The water pressure at a depth of 4 miles

66

is about 10,000 pounds per square inch force. But there are other ways of simulating 'feel', for the purpose of grasping objects for example. Television cameras and microphones would provide the primary channels of information on which the operator might base his decisions.

Remote control at its most ambitious level, of a piece of space engineering from an earthbound 'cockpit', has been envisaged by an American engineer, William E. Bradley, in a telechiric control concept he described to an aerospace conference in Boston in 1966. Man and machine can be linked, he believes, so that by performing the manœuvres himself the man would cause them to take place at distances of thousands of miles. In this way man could control a spacecraft or satellite or assemble a space station with no less ease than if he were on the spot. (More, perhaps, for he would not be hampered by a space-suit or by prevailing conditions of gravity or acceleration.) But the same ideas could find their widest application in cable-less telechirics right here on Earth.

Bradley, who developed his idea for the U.S. Defense Department at the Institute for Defense Analyses, a 'think tank' in Arlington, Virginia, bases his control on a miniature television screen mounted on the head of the operator, in such a way that when he moves his head the remote television camera would follow. In this way his view would change perspective just as if he were on the spot, and he could judge distance by making use of the parallax produced by small movements of his head.

A sketch of the scheme appears in Fig. 11. The operator would move many mechanical degrees of freedom continuously and simultaneously, without conscious attention to each one individually. In this respect it would be as though he were performing the task himself. For this reason the harness he used to control the process would need to be geometrically similar to man's own skeletal structure, so that the operator suffered no distraction in making unfamiliar manœuvres. The telefactor, as this telechiric is called, could be made much larger and more powerful or much smaller than a man, if need be — a refinement to which we return below.

One important point about Bradley's scheme is that all the information required for mechanical control could be carried by conventional methods of telemetry, using the quite modest band-

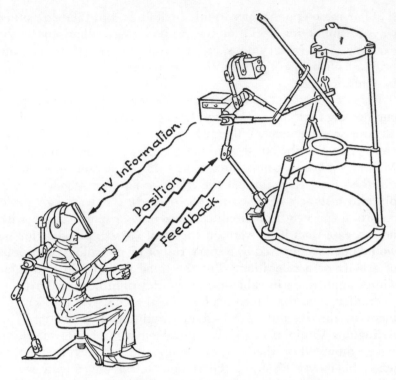

FIG. 11. The telefactor concept of very remote control

width of about 4 kilocycles, allowing about 100 cycles apiece for, say, 32 degrees of freedom. The force feedback to the operator could also be contained within such a bandwidth. Unfortunately the time delay would prevent the operator working in 'real time' over distances greater than about 30,000 miles, when he would be restricted to an 'open loop' of taking actions without waiting to see the consequences.

Since a human operator moves relatively slowly, and exerts only small forces, seldom more than a few pounds, the amount of power involved would not be great, and a total drain of 150 watts is foreseen by Bradley as covering both the workload and the demands of telemetry. Several telefactors could collaborate, of course, in which event the team leader alone need manipulate the all-seeing camera, minimizing the bandwidth and power needed.

Proceeding in parallel with the telechiric or 'distant hand'

68

approach to remote control are various schemes for the direct amplification of the operator's movements; for example, the weapon-aiming system for pilots developed by the Philco Corporation for the U.S. Air Force. Early in the First World War bombs were aimed by the simple expedient of the bombardier twisting the pilot's head, whereupon the pilot would re-align his machine on to the target. (A similar expedient was adopted in some tanks, where the tank commander directed his driver—who could not see the way ahead—by means of strategically placed kicks.) The Philco system provides the pilot with a helmet that is coupled by a servo-system so that he can take approximate aim merely by swivelling his head. The fine aim that fires his weapon is attained by the reflection of a tiny spot of infra-red light from his own eyes when he is looking straight ahead at his target.

The military machine has many potential applications for 'man-amplifiers', such as the 'starlight' system of image intensification that can give the soldier night vision, by sensing the different amounts of infra-red emanating from different objects in the scene he is viewing. In fact, a major goal of military infra-red research is the equipping of every serviceman with microminiature viewers, perhaps no larger than contact lenses, that would give him true night-time vision.

Another project, sponsored jointly by the U.S. Army and Navy, the prototype of which is taking shape in General Electric's laboratories, is an exo-skeleton, or external skeleton, that will give its wearer a lifting capacity of three-quarters of a ton. The idea is that this 'walking manipulator', called Hardiman, will be used for many kinds of hard labour—bomb-loading, underwater assembly work, and so on—using motions that are essentially natural. The operator will simply step inside his hydraulically powered skeleton, when a weight of 1,500 pounds will feel no heavier than 60 pounds, and he will raise it 6 feet in 5 or 6 seconds.

Behind Hardiman lie several years of experimental work on systems that will extend man's physical capacity yet preserve the flexibility that allows him to make a score or even more different controlled actions simultaneously (see Plate 9). Work in the Cornell Aeronautical Laboratory, Buffalo, New York, with an unpowered exo-skeleton has helped to define some of the requirements—and shown, incidentally, that the problem has much in common with the design of orthotic and prosthetic systems for bracing and replacing human limbs.

The ultimate objective, according to project engineer Ralph Mosher, is nothing less than a situation in which the operator achieves a mental transference, with the machine becoming an extension of himself. 'No longer must the operator condition himself to the machine or learn and think about the operation involved. Man and machine become a single integrated function system, with the operator concentrating wholly on the task in hand.'

The exo-skeleton will not be limited in size. There is no apparent reason why a 50-foot exo-skeleton should not perform in the same way as smaller ones do, provided force and position information are appropriately scaled down. Take walking, for example, a procedure described by one anatomist as 'a unique activity during which the body, step by step, teeters on the edge of catastrophe'.[5] The subtleties of control that permit us to perform this complex manœuvre with confidence and skill might most usefully be transferred to a walking machine like Pedipulator (see Plate 10). Another General Electric project is the development of a 'walking truck', 12 feet long and 10 feet tall, capable of carrying 500 pounds at about 5 miles an hour. The front legs of this quadruped will be controlled by the operator's arms, the rear ones by his legs, using motions akin to those a skier employs. The same team has also designed a mechanical horse that can be ridden over very rough terrain at 30 m.p.h., as an exercise for the U.S. Army.

Scaled *down* in size and strength, however, the exo-skeleton affords possibilities no less exciting: in surgery, for example, where by damping down hand tremors it could make a big contribution to microsurgery, or might allow the surgeon to operate remotely, from outside a sterile barrier and even at a great distance from his patient.

There are many problems to be resolved before man and machine become fully integrated. The engineer needs to know exactly how much and what kind of information is necessary for the operator to take appropriate action under given circumstances. In a walking machine, for example, he must see that the operator receives enough information to avoid any risk of stumbling, for if this were to happen machine and operator would probably sprawl in quite different ways. This could have the most alarming consequences when the operator tried to regain his feet.

One unusually interesting prospect in man-machine integration is of short-circuiting the actuators—the hands and feet—and coupling the machine straight into the central nervous system. Unfortunately, we do not yet know how to 'plug into' the nervous system directly. But we can make a very useful indirect coupling by way of the muscles that operate the human actuators.

On contraction these muscles generate small electric currents, known as 'myo-electric' currents, which can be tapped from the surface of the skin by suitably sensitive electrodes, or even at source by electrodes buried in the muscle. When amplified and sorted, these signals can be used as control signals for the machine, with a significantly better speed of response. There are still plenty of problems—we shall meet some of them in Chapter 3, where the possibility is examined of using myo-electric signals to operate an artificial limb—but already attempts are being made to use such a coupling between man and the machine he is operating.

One application, a development of which is sponsored by the

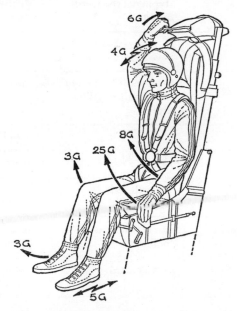

FIG. 12. Movement is just possible under the accelerations indicated

U.S. Navy, could aid the pilot of a high-performance aircraft who finds his movements cramped by the effect of very high forces of acceleration (see Fig. 12). In this way he might, almost literally, 'will' his arm to perform.

AMPLIFYING THE MENTAL PROCESSES

The computer is a machine capable of 'thinking' about a million times as fast as a man—and more than a million times as accurately. This makes it an extremely powerful machine by human standards. An expensive machine too, for when microminiaturized no piece of advanced technology costs more per pound.

TABLE *Brain versus computer*

	BRAIN	COMPUTER
'Reset' time of elements	10^{-2} second	10^{-7} second
Rate of transfer information	10–30 bits/second (typing at 200 words/ minute)	6,000 bits/second (higher with magnetic tape)
Storage rate	< 1 bit/second in long-term memory	> 10^6 bits/second
Storage capacity	theoretical maximum 10^9 bits during lifetime	currently 3×10^7 bits
Processing	parallel	serial
Interconnections	rich	poor
Filtering	very efficient	receives only predigested information
Effects of component failure	rarely produces 'nonsense'	usually produces 'nonsense'
Type of problems that can be tackled	very general	rather limited

N.B. Figures are only rough approximations; computer data, particularly of capacity, are still changing very rapidly (after *Science Journal*).

It is not easy even to make contact with such a machine, except at very low levels of efficiency, simply because its electronic circuits perform so much faster than any mechanical system used to interrogate it. A typewriter keyboard, the most commonplace means of contact, is limited to the speed of typing, say 200 words a minute, compared with speech delivered at perhaps 120 words a minute. And everyone is well aware how easily the brain can race ahead of the words of someone who is speaking to us.

The great selling point for the computer during the decade or so that it has been available commercially has been its ability to absorb and catalogue vast amounts of information (see Table). It has been presented as a high-speed idiot that does only what it is told to do (although paradoxically there were jeers when it appeared to make a mistake, like paying someone a very large sum of money or deducting too much from an account). The approach served to launch the machine on a suspicious and reluctant world of business but, as scientists long have appreciated, it sadly under-estimates the machine's true potential.

The computer amplifies the mental processes in two ways: by accelerating the rate of calculation, and by extending the capacity of the memory. Incidental to these advantages is the far better accuracy, unhampered by 'tricks of memory' unless they have been injected by the human operator.

The machine has four essential components (see Fig. 13), known colloquially as the 'hardware'. The *memory* (or store) retains the program of instructions and the key to its use, along with any information the machine itself has generated and still requires. The *central processor* or arithmetic unit is where the calculations are made, on information drawn from the memory. The *input* and *output* units, collectively known as the peripherals, are the organs whereby the computer receives data and presents the consequences of its cogitation.

The program of instructions is known as the 'software'. Written in special maths-based language, its preparation for the more sophisticated applications of the computer can be a slow and highly skilled process that costs no less than the computer itself.

The electronic computer has developed at such a pace that technically it can appear overwhelmingly complex. In point of fact, however, for all but its most esoteric applications it has now

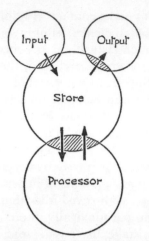

FIG. 13. Essential parts of a computer, and their interaction

stabilized in basic design, with the appearance in 1965 of the
'series' concept, the essence of which is a catalogue of interchange-
able units that can be extended or contracted at will, and with
which all new developments will mate for several, perhaps many,
years to come. In this way the machine is arranged to match the
user's requirements at a given time while remaining free to take
advantage of each new advance as it arrives.

In the foregoing remarks the emphasis has been on the essential
simplicity of the computer. But there is one fundamental difference
between man and this machine that, so far, has hindered any true
symbiosis, and this is the dissimilarity between the two thought
processes. Man thinks mostly in words—language—while the
digital computer can 'think' only in figures. This means that, in
order to program the computer, a process nowadays equated with
the teaching or training of a child, the human operator must communicate in a special maths-based language. It is the language and
the fluency with which it is employed that chiefly determines how
successful a symbiosis is attained between man and machine.

Input units are the eyes and ears of the computer, output units
its voice and its limbs. But there has been great disparity between
their speed of response and that of the computer itself—a disparity
that is responsible for one of the most important areas of development in computer 'hardware' today.

74

Most computers at present feed upon data in the form of punched cards or punched paper tape, prepared on a typewriter type of keyboard: a comparatively slow but clear and unambiguous mode of presentation. But far more sophisticated methods are needed to bring the computer into close communion with man. One of the most exciting has its origins in a Ph.D. thesis undertaken in 1961 by Ivan Sutherland, a scientist at the Massachusetts Institute of Technology. Using an electronic stylus, the operator can write or sketch on the face of a TV-type display—just as he might on the back of an envelope. Sketchpad, as Sutherland called his system, takes the fluorescing lines so formed on the tube and refashions them into geometric forms, enlarges, rotates or replicates, shifts or shrinks them to order.

Just how closely Sketchpad brings the operator into communion with the computer may be gauged from Sutherland's own experience, quoted in Gilbert Burck's book *The Computer Age*: 'It's like flying a jet plane. You have a machine that can do a lot for you if you treat it right. I spent hours with it, at times when there was no one to interrupt me, and it was a thrill to struggle with an idea and then to see it working on the screen.'[6]

The principles of Sketchpad are proving applicable elsewhere, in engineering design especially (see Plate 11); while the Lockheed Aircraft Corporation has developed a 'video matrix terminal', essentially a closed-circuit TV system that can call up from a computer a display of its knowledge of a patient and his possible treatment. The doctor or surgeon can then use an electronic stylus to add his own judgments and instructions. Such a system has been installed at the Mayo Clinic in Rochester, Minnesota.

But techniques of this sort call for a very large and powerful computer a display of its knowledge of a patient and his possible memory. Small machines undoubtedly have their uses, for quick calculations or the control of individual processes, for example, but as a leading I.B.M. scientist, Dr J. C. R. Licklider, has put it: 'A slow computer or a computer with a small memory does not make a very fascinating intellectual partner. If the memory cycle is less than 10 microseconds and the memory larger than 4,000 words, however, one can sense the presence of significant power and, with the aid of sensitive programming, can develop an intellectual partner worthy of the name.'[7]

Large, powerful computers, however, are costly machines. If their power is to be made readily available, some way must be found of making maximum use of their speed so that a very large number of people can use the same machine simultaneously. This is the philosophy of 'time-sharing', also known as 'multiple access', that today is in the mainstream of computer development. The problem, quite simply, is to develop a machine and a program that allows hundreds, even thousands, of operators to 'plug into' it as freely as they would tap the electricity network for electric power, without getting their wires crossed.

One of the most ambitious time-sharing schemes in the world today is Project MAC—'multiple-access computer' or 'machine-aided cognition'—at the Massachusetts Institute of Technology, where two I.B.M. 7094 computers provide a mass memory of 36 million words. By the spring of 1967, 160 teletype terminals throughout the U.S.A. were connected to MAC's memory, and up to thirty people could 'plug in' simultaneously.

The implications of so powerful an amplifier as this (and several similar schemes) are immense. They could even change society as we know it today. In a paper to a symposium on 'New horizons in science and engineering' in New York in 1967, Dr R. M. Fano, who is in charge of MAC, observed that many of society's rules and regulations stem from the fact that chaos would result unless the behaviour of people were predictable. But the computer could allow society to be more diverse in its actions, more flexible in its regulations and laws. This is because the machine has the information-processing capacity to cater for individual idiosyncrasies where present methods would be time-consuming and costly.

Beyond these developments lies the prospect of speaking directly to the computer—and of the machine responding by means of the spoken word. The incentive to pursue a machine that can 'hear' is provided by telephony, the latest electronic exchanges for which are essentially big computing machines. With numbers growing steadily longer, there is a powerful pull to simplify things for the subscriber to the point where he might speak the number or service he wants straight into the mouthpiece, for immediate attention by the automatic exchange.

The difficulties that attend even so straightforward a set of instructions as the numbers nought to nine are immense, as

76

Japanese scientists discovered in their efforts to build a phonetic typewriter: 'Our speech synthesizer may seem ready for application. However, the spoken digit samples we use are uttered at relatively constant levels, and picked up in a quiet room. When these comparatively severe conditions are not satisfied, the performance appears to deteriorate considerably.'[8] The difficulties appear to lie in successfully compressing for the computer the surprisingly large amount of information we can convey in the most casual utterance.

But machines that not merely respond to the spoken word but actually talk back to the operator are already a possibility. In the spring of 1967 I visited a Japanese government laboratory on the outskirts of Tokyo where a computer 'recited', in Japanese, a traditional fairy tale. These scientists, at the Electrotechnical Laboratory, were developing an analogue speech synthesizer as part of the laboratory's programme on automatic translation. They promised that if I were to return in a year or so their I.B.M. 7090 computer would render [sic] 'an English fairy tale by Aesop or Grimm'.

Ultimately, there is the prospect of bypassing the body's own peripheral mechanisms altogether, by employing some form of thought transference to communicate directly with the machine. An American Air Force scientist has already taught people — himself amongst them — to 'think' simple messages into a computer. The messages are transmitted in the form of Morse code; long and short bursts of alpha activity, a powerful electrical activity of around ten cycles a second believed to be associated with the brain. Dr Edmond Dewan of the Air Force Cambridge Research Laboratories, Bedford, Massachusetts, used an E.E.G. pattern as part of his computer program.[9] The bursts of alpha activity, tapped by electrodes affixed to the forehead and filtered to remove spurious signals, were translated by the computer into letters that it printed out automatically on a teleprinter.

Although at first sight the prospect of communicating one's thoughts directly to a computer is a fascinating one, it remains fairly remote. Speed of thought transference is a serious handicap. It took Dr Dewan and his subjects about thirty-five seconds to think a single letter into the machine, while the incidence of inaccuracies was high.

The human body, as we found in Chapter 1, is a complex of systems—blood, respiratory, nervous, and so on—all interdependent and intimately interacting to keep us alive and in good working order. Even at this quite primitive stage of its development the computer can already make an important contribution to the ailing human mechanism. For example, Russian surgeons at the Institute of Experimental Medicine in Leningrad use a computer in the course of a brain operation to correct a disorder of bodily control.

During this operation, bundles of fine gold wires are inserted into the thalamus region of the brain, a critical area responsible for the unconscious movements of the body. The computer, guided by X-ray photographs, calculates exactly where and how deep each wire must be placed, to within a millimetre. A few days later the thirty or forty wires implanted under the computer's guidance are used as electrodes to explore the malfunctioning of this part of the brain.

There is no reason in principle why a computer should not run an entire laboratory—calibrating its own instruments, detecting and correcting any malfunction, carrying out assays and measurements, and recording the data; in short, carrying out all the activities one might expect from an accurate but unimaginative laboratory technician. A concept for a computer-managed laboratory for use in space was advanced by I.B.M. scientists at an aerospace conference in Seattle in 1967. But they saw their machine used in intimate association with Earthbound experimenters—they admitted that 'there is no present substitute on these higher levels for that kind of scientific insight prompted by exceptional results that often leads to truly exciting discovery'. In other words, their computer-managed laboratory would take things to the point of saying 'Here's some data—what now?'

Still more intimate is the relationship between computer and patient foreseen by some surgeons, where the patient will actually be 'on-line' with a machine that adjusts and compensates for the slightest variation from whatever is judged to be 'normal'. The idea is already being used for the intensive care of cardiac patients. A computer system that monitors the E.C.G. waveform of a severely ill patient, and can give up to forty minutes' warning of an impending heart attack, has been developed by medical staff with the Barnet General Hospital near London. This system avoids the difficulties a computer still has in actually recognizing a pattern, in this case a waveform, by responding only to a pattern that is changing. It converts the complexities of the E.C.G. into a much simpler waveform from which the nurse can easily detect any trend towards a deterioration or improvement in the heart's behaviour.

Taken a little further, the computer will be used to monitor the progress of a patient throughout the operation, and during the pre-operative and recovery periods too. Not only the E.C.G. but other fast-changing factors like blood pressure and the respiratory waveform, along with more slowly changing factors like temperature and heart rate, will all come under continuous surveillance and control, and moreover displayed in 'real time' — as it is happening — in graphic form on a screen, right in the operating theatre. As a British physicist working to this end once put it to me, 'The patient will be like an engine on a test bed.' Nor is the idea limited to the operating room, for research workers with the Case Institute of Technology have restored some mobility to the arms of a most severely disabled patient by placing him 'on-line' with a computer, as we shall see in the next chapter.

Drs Stephen Abrahamson and J. S. Denson of the University of Southern California's School of Medicine have applied the computer in another ingenious way, to organize one of the most complex medical teaching aids yet devised. This is a computer-controlled manikin for training anaesthetists (see Plate 12), complete with tongue, teeth, epiglottis, vocal cords, trachea and bronchial tubes. SIM 1, as it is called, has a heart-beat, carotid and temporal pulse-beats and blood pressure. Its chest and diaphragm move as it 'breathes', its eyes open and close, and its pupils dilate and constrict. Certain drugs will cause the muscles of this 195-pound manikin to twitch, its brow to wrinkle. The manikin may choke, have a heart attack, pass out altogether.

But sophisticated as this simulator is in its responses, it was conceived as just the first of a family that will take the surgeon from the airway to the chest, head, ear, nose, teeth, abdomen and extremities. Future simulators, says Dr Abrahamson, will perspire, salivate, even bleed.

Beyond even the most lifelike simulator, however, is the prospect of computer diagnosis. The overwhelming difficulty here, of course, is the haphazard nature of the progress whereby a doctor normally examines a patient, makes a diagnosis (perhaps in consultation with other doctors) and arrives at a course of treatment. We know too little about the performance of the normal, healthy body, while the doctor may be guided enormously—although not necessarily accurately—by his personal knowledge of the patient and his idiosyncrasies.

One area in which computer-aided diagnosis is already being explored is psychological diagnosis. At a symposium on 'The art of listening' held in Sheffield in 1966, a British general practitioner, Dr W. J. H. Lord, told his colleagues that 'many general practitioners are unable to carry out a mental examination with the same skill as they can carry out a physical examination'. He went on to describe a computer program compiled at the Stanford Research Institute in California that carries out limited psychotherapeutic dialogues and 'is designed to communicate an intent to help as a psychotherapist does, and to respond in questioning, clarifying, focusing, rephrasing and occasionally interpreting the subject's answer … Although the communications are written, the dialogue has many of the properties of a spoken conversation; it is reported to be dynamic and demands an immediate reply. It strives to evoke as well as to express.'

A simple computer capable of infiltrating a person's mind in much the same way as a hypnotist is being developed by a British psychiatrist. Dr John Clarke of the University of Manchester foresees applications for his machine in several branches of medicine; childbirth, dentistry and psychiatric treatment among them. His ideas are based on the thesis that the hypnotist is actually a teacher, and the technique of inducing hypnosis is an example of programmed instruction. But his computer logic attempts to simulate only the stereotyped portions of the hypnotist's technique, leaving its human operator the tasks of first gaining the subject's confidence and also selecting the appropriate questions to be put.

Dr Clarke has, in effect, programmed his computer with a peculiarly hypnotic kind of text. Tape-recorded suggestions are played to the subject, seated in an armchair with wings that prevent his head from rolling too far sideways. He is invited at intervals to press a button. For example, the machine, having suggested that the subject's eyes are slowly closing, asks him to press the button if his eyes have already closed. Each time the subject responds by pressing the button, he is taken by further suggestions to another, still deeper level of hypnosis. In other words, he programs himself into hypnosis — at his own pace.

Man is equipped with not one but two metabolisms, suggests Sir Julian Huxley: 'Two systems for transforming the raw materials of nature in serviceable ways. Physiological metabolism utilizes the raw materials of objective nature and elaborates them into biologically operative physico-chemical compounds and systems. Psychometabolism on the other hand utilizes the raw materials of subjective or mind-accompanied experience and elaborates them into psychosocially operative organizations of thought and feeling ... '[10]

We shall return to the idea in the final chapter, although in fact it pervades the rest of this book.

CHAPTER THREE

Man Augmented

'The body is just something to carry the brain around in.'

Thomas Alva Edison

THE symbiosis between man and machine we explored in the previous chapter has the purpose of extending man's natural limits. Somewhat different is the philosophy that guides attempts to match man and machine in order to replace or restore some function, deficient as a consequence of accident, disease or congenital deformity.

For one thing, the very fact that the person is deficient in some physical respect is often a handicap both technically and psychologically: technically, because the disabled person is not usually the best person to acquire fresh, perhaps complex skills; psychologically, because so many whole and healthy people seem to find difficulty in accepting that a physical disability is not normally accompanied by some mental insufficiency.

But the most serious obstacle at the moment is that we simply do not know how to 'plug into' the central nervous system, other than in the crudest and most empirical manner. To be able to do so might give us control over the electrical signals from the brain itself.

A human limb is an astonishingly versatile mechanism, and any attempt to simulate its full range of freedoms with the technology we have at present seems bound to lead to an untenably complicated substitute. The difficulty lies not so much in miniaturizing suitable power sources and control mechanisms but in arranging for the powered limb to work harmoniously with the living body.

It is one thing to integrate a fully fit and highly trained person intimately with a complex machine like an aircraft or one of the telechiric systems discussed in the previous chapter. But quite another to expect someone who is already handicapped physically, and who in age, intelligence and sex may be drawn from any sector of the community, to adapt readily to a difficult and wholly alien mode of controlling his new limb, which of itself cannot but be complex if it is to simulate the real thing.

To quote one American scientist, Dr Ralph Alter of the Massachusetts Institute of Technology, on this point: 'Complexity in and of itself is completely irrelevant to the amputee; rather it is the complexity of the control operations which the amputee must perform, for motions which may in fact be very simple, which matters.'[1]

Until quite recently there was little effort to power an artificial limb at all. Although Ambroise Paré, the French military surgeon, was devising some remarkably sophisticated mechanical hands and arms for soldiers in the mid-sixteenth century, his aim was primarily a cosmetic one, and his prostheses were no more self-actuating than, say, artificial teeth. But several factors have intervened during the present century to raise interest rapidly in this quarter. Two world wars and the motor car have between them claimed many hundreds of thousands of limbs; while advancing medical practice ensures both that amputees live longer and that far more elderly people now survive the loss of a limb through disease.

Then, too, for reasons of which we are still unsure, occasionally a baby is born with an undeveloped limb, often having instead a flipper-like appendage that gives the deformity its medical name of phocomelia (from the Greek words *phoke*, meaning seal, and *melos*, limb). Sometimes even the flipper is absent and the condition is then called amelia. These are very rare afflictions, but in 1962 the world was alerted to what was virtually an epidemic, so savage that usually two and even all four limbs were affected. The cause was a drug called thalidomide, hitherto regarded as complacently as aspirin—and sometimes dispensed almost as freely. It was subsequently shown to possess one of the most horrifying of flaws for a pharmaceutical product—teratogenicity, the capacity to produce a 'monster'.

83

This drug was not dispensed in the U.S.A., but Ministry of Health figures for the period during which thalidomide was marketed in Britain (1957–61) indicate that 349 babies were probably deformed as a consequence of the mother taking this drug during those few weeks of gestation when the foetal limb buds were beginning to develop, compared with 545 malformed babies for which there was no cause to indict the drug. Germany fared far worse and has more than 3,000 victims of thalidomide (sold there as Contergan) alive today; Japan (nearly 1,000 originally and about 200 still living) and Canada (74 still alive in 1963) were other countries that suffered. One consequence in all four countries has been the greatly heightened interest in powered artificial limbs.

So far more attention, both before and since the thalidomide tragedy, has been paid to the upper limbs, for the obvious reason that the great majority of our physical skills are communicated by way of the arms and hands. The victims of thalidomide present more complex problems than amputees for several reasons, among them the wide variety of their deformities, which can range from almost complete limbs to no limbs whatsoever, and the fact that the patients are young and still growing. Emotional factors too have sometimes obscured the technical points at issue.

Amputations on the other hand are usually made at one of a relatively small number of sites, and careful surgery and nursing can go far towards preparing the stump for the fitting of a prosthesis. In the words of Dr Miroslaw Vitali of the Ministry of Health's Limb Fitting Centre in London: 'Amputation is not an operation of destruction but is rather one of construction to form a new organ of locomotion and so make the patient mobile again.'[2]

We have a situation today where the more advanced countries of the world have a large and growing population of people lacking one or more limbs, an increasing proportion of which are elderly. The U.S.A. for example has about half a million amputees, only about 40,000 of which are war veterans. One 'guesstimate' gives Russia a total of 800,000. Britain has about 90,000, and adds 4,700 annually, while some 60 per cent are over sixty years old. Moreover, British statistics indicate that the majority of elderly patients with vascular disease (of the blood vessels) who live another five years after an amputation become double amputees.

Until now artificial arms have derived their (limited) power by harnessing some other body movement such as a shrug of the shoulder, which provides the wearer with control over at least one movement of his prosthesis. A more sophisticated approach was actually tried quite widely early in the present century. It aimed to use the muscles of the stump in a manner not dissimilar from their original role. The idea was so to modify the muscle by surgery that when flexed it would pull upon a control cable. This was done by plastic surgery, in creating a skin-lined 'tunnel' through the muscle, through which a pin could be passed to pull the cable.

The advantage of 'cineplasty', as the operation was known, was that it permitted a more natural action to be used to move the artificial limb. The drawbacks proved first to be the difficulty of keeping the new tunnel clean and free from infection; and also that it meant a surgical modification of the body that was perhaps ahead of its time, and which both the patient and those close to him seemed to find hard to accept. For those two reasons the operation is little practised today.

Interest now focuses on limbs powered by other means. The source of this power is not too important. Pneumatic power, from a gas such as carbon dioxide stored under pressure, or electric power from batteries are the obvious sources, each having certain advantages and some significant limitations at present. What is very important—and difficult—however is how the wearer exercises control over this prosthesis.

At its crudest this control can be exercised by pushing buttons with the other hand or the toes. At its most sophisticated it would be done merely by 'willing' the motion required; and anything short of this is alien—non-physiological—and must be learned. At the present stage of development of powered limbs interest centres on the use of myo-electric currents, the small electrical signals of up to 25 millivolts generated by a muscle fibre when it contracts, to exercise control over one or more movements of a prosthesis.

In the U.S.A. credit is usually given to the late Dr Norbert Weiner for first suggesting, in the early 1950s, the possibility of using these myo-electric currents to control the motions of a prosthesis. The signal can be picked up quite easily by a sensitive electrode pressed against the skin over the muscle. In this way the currents generated by the remaining muscles of a forearm stump might be detected, amplified and employed to control, say, the rotation of a prosthetic wrist. By the mid-1950s, research teams led by Nightingale in Britain and Kobrinsky in Russia had developed simple forearm prostheses that operated in this way.

Nightingale's work at St Thomas's and Guy's Hospitals in London, more recently pursued by Dr Alastair Bottomley[3] while with the Medical Research Council's Centre for Muscle Substitutes (now the Powered Limbs Research Unit) in London, has led to one of the more highly engineered of artificial arms. This is also a forearm prosthesis, the original design of which has recently been refined and miniaturized in the laboratories of the Atomic Weapons Research Establishment at Aldermaston. This system uses the natural signals from the flexor and extensor muscle groups in the forearm, picked up from the surface of the skin. They are amplified, rectified and smoothed, to give a d.c. signal closely proportional to the force demanded of the muscle by the central nervous system (see Fig. 14). To overcome the effect of 'crosstalk'

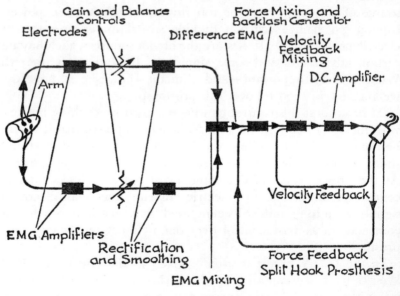

FIG. 14. Circuit of the myo-electrically controlled Bottomley forearm prosthesis, developed by the Medical Research Council

86

—signals picked up from the wrong muscle—the d.c. signals (of about a millivolt from the skin) from the two opposing muscle groups are subtracted. Thus a signal is generated proportional in amplitude to the force demanded by the muscle, and whose polarity decides the direction of this force.

The latest Bottomley prosthesis (see Plate 13) has been designed to use two kinds of 'hand'. The hook, giving a firm three-point grip of up to ten pounds, which is generally preferred for work, can be unplugged and exchanged for a 'cosmetic prosthesis' in the shape of a Dorrance hand, where thumb and first two fingers are 'active' and move towards one another in a caliper motion, to provide a maximum fingertip force of six pounds. Power is drawn from a twenty-ounce battery strapped to the back of the wearer, along with the fifteen-ounce control unit.

Russian progress with the myo-electric principle (which they call 'bio-electric') appears further advanced, at least in its application. Alexander Kennaway, a British consultant on prosthetics to the Ministry of Health, who visited the Moscow Institute of Prosthetics on the Ministry's behalf in 1966, learned that more than 1,000 myo-electric forearm prostheses had already been fitted, compared with just a handful in Britain at that time. The Russian system is very similar to that of the Bottomley hand, but their greater experience has revealed such points as the unduly low muscle voltages found in amputees of long standing and also when the amputee is insufficiently trained. This engineer was also shown a prototype artificial hand which he reported was potentially a considerable improvement on anything else he had seen, in which all five fingers are capable of closing around objects of any shape.

The big difficulty in developing prostheses which are much more complex than an artificial arm with a few simple actions is one of finding enough control sites. Quite simply, the more functions one needs to replace, the fewer there remain to harness for their control.

A single living arm has a great many degrees of freedom, far more than one could contemplate building into a prosthesis without complicating life unbearably for the wearer. More control sites might be harnessed if, for example, the signals could be identified more selectively, perhaps by implanting electrodes within the muscles, and sorting the signals by means of a computer system of pattern recognition. British scientists are experimenting with small aerials buried beneath the skin, which can relay E.M.G. signals to an electronic circuit outside the body. But there comes a point beyond which increasing versatility yields diminishing returns. An unconscious gesticulation, for example, may delight both the patient and his mentors but it will also soak up power uselessly.

Dr David Simpson, a physicist with the Princess Margaret Rose Orthopaedic Hospital in Edinburgh, is equipping Scotland's score or so of thalidomide victims with pairs of artificial arms, one powered and the other passive. His aim is a powered limb that is versatile, having six degrees of freedom, yet simple enough for the child to come to use instinctively—to eat, to dress, to use the lavatory, to handle pen and paper, for example; in fact to become reasonably independent of other people. He aims not merely to create an attachment but to establish between the limb and its owner the kind of symbiosis one finds between a good driver and his car. This ambitious blend of properties Simpson calls 'dynamic cosmesis'.

'We were impressed by the fact that in general the essential property which the wearer wishes to control is the position of the prosthesis and we therefore designed a control system specifically directed to control position.'[4] In short, the position of the prosthesis —or more specifically of the hand itself—is directly controlled by the position of a control lever that itself is moved by some other part of the body, by shrugging or hunching the shoulders, for example. This establishes a link between 'mechanical physiology' and natural physiology, that removes the need for the wearer always to be closely watching the behaviour of his prosthesis. In this way, Dr Simpson believes, it is possible to control several movements simultaneously.

Rather than attempt to simulate the complexities of the living arm (which in any case have no meaning for the congenitally armless person), Simpson is attempting to restore the primary function of the arm, which is to position the hand in space. This can be done, he contends, by a mechanism that controls the following three factors: (1) the distance of the hand from the shoulder, (2) its angle of elevation to the shoulder, and (3) its

88

angle of azimuth: in other words, near and far, up and down, and left to right.

Such a prosthesis would use the theoretical minimum number of controls — three — in addition to which the wearer would require two more: to control rotation of the wrist and the grip of the hand. These five controls could be exercised even by someone with bilateral amelia — no arms whatsoever — through 'joysticks' or control levers on each shoulder plus a neck movement. Most significant of all, however, such controls could be used intuitively by the wearer.

At the same time Dr Simpson is highly conscious of the aesthetic aspects of his mechanisms: that they should not be noisy or move with grotesque, puppet-like motions, for example. Already, with their early models, he and his colleagues have been gratified to find the children making unconscious, instinctive movements with their 'hands' — gesticulating, running their fingers through their hair, even picking their noses.

Fully developed, such a mechanism should provide much of the function of a normal arm. It could also be valuable to an almost immobilized person, as a bedside attachment that would need the minimum of physical effort to give him at least some independence; or, in quite another context, to give an aircraft pilot almost immobilized by the forces of acceleration (see Fig. 12) continuing control over his machine.

Another application that is being explored for the very versatile hydraulic arms illustrated in Plate 14 is the possibility of replicating the manipulations of an operator, on an assembly line, for example.

Even the problems of total paralysis, from the neck down, are finding relief in prosthetic systems today. One technical hurdle, of course, is to make a mechanical connection between the brain, which is normally unimpaired, and the external controls. In Britain a small band of enthusiasts working in their spare time with patients in the National Spinal Injuries Centre at Stoke Mandeville Hospital developed a system of 'patient-operated selector mechanisms' (P.O.S.M. or Possums) that harness whatever residual physical motions the patient may possess, and amplify or extend them. Since even the most severely disabled must retain control of the mouth and breathing, the P.O.S.M.

team has concentrated upon controls operated by this means. At first they endeavoured to harness the air flow, but found it required quite a volume even to blow a whistle—the simplest and most obvious alarm system. They then turned to pressure, which they found to afford a less taxing and highly sensitive mode of control. Harnessed to the keyboard of an electric typewriter, even simple controls of this kind permit typing speeds of thirty to forty words a minute.

This approach takes care of the worst kinds of disability, but very often there are small residual muscular movements in the fingers or the toes that can be amplified in the same way. A pressure of only three grams or a movement of one-thousandth of an inch are enough to trip the microswitch. The P.O.S.M. Research Project, as it is now known, has devised a control system for an electric car that uses only the tips of three fingers and the thumb of the left hand of a tetraplegic—one paralysed in all four limbs—so that he can drive it by 'remote control'. The vehicle, a converted milk-float, allows its driver to travel up to 16 miles on a single recharge, at a top speed of 7 m.p.h., and still leaves him enough control capacity to contact his home by radio.

One of the latest 'Possums' is an electric typewriter that can be operated by the mouth at typing speeds of up to 100 words a minute. This requires a coded input, based on two levels of pressure and two more of suction. When used in conjunction with a loudspeaking telephone and a tape-recorder, it equips the tetraplegic with the basic requirements to run a one-man business (see Plate 15). The same principles are applicable to any other kind of equipment that uses a keyboard input, from machine tools to computers.

'A recent lunch was one of the most dramatic events of Edward Roszak's life. Trailing wires and wearing thick-rimmed glasses attached to electrodes and more wires, he was wheeled over to a table and he began to feed himself. To casual onlookers at Highland View Hospital in Cleveland, Ohio, it seemed a slow, cumbersome way to eat. But they were unaware that three years before it had seemed unlikely that Roszak would ever use his arms or legs again.'[5]

Thus begins a description by two members of the Cybernetic Systems Group at the Case Institute of Technology of their efforts to harness a paralysed muscle by routing the messages through another muscle and an electronic stimulator. In 1963 Thomas and Crochetière, two researchers at Highland View, made what they believed to be the first attempt to use the myo-electric currents from one muscle to stimulate another. But when amplified to 70 volts at a frequency of 10 kilohertz, the impulse caused Crochetière momentarily to faint. When Luiji Vodonik and William D. McLeod came to repeat the work they were careful

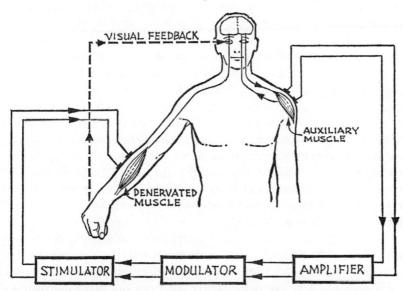

Fig. 15. Electrical bypass to the lesion that prevents direct control of the arm, under development at the Case Institute of Technology. Myo-electric signals from another muscle are harnessed to drive circuits that stimulate the paralysed muscle

to keep the two stimulating electrodes very close together, so that the connection drew a minimum of current.

Their scheme is sketched in Fig. 15. The trapezius (shoulder) muscle provides the initial stimulus, which is amplified, modulated and used to drive the electronic stimulator, the output from which is fed into the denervated muscle. In this way Edward Roszak (a tetraplegic) and others have retrained their hands to grasp such articles as cutlery, using a simple visual 'feedback' to keep conscious control of the process. So much did Roszak become part of the research team that his name appeared on some of its published work, although he has since left the hospital to lead his own life.

Another five of Roszak's arm movements were arranged through a powered splint (see also Plate 16), these being rotation of the shoulder and the upper arm, its movement towards and away from the body, bending of the elbow, and twisting of the wrist. Roszak wore spectacles, the frame of which carried a small lamp. He could throw its light upon an array of photo-cells ranged before him, to select a tape-recorded program that controlled one of the five arm motions. The arm itself was driven pneumatically by compressed carbon dioxide, through the splint, in much the same way as some of the artificial arms described earlier.

An extension of this system of electronic detours to more than one limb means the patient must learn a wholly alien pattern of control that now becomes very complicated indeed. The computer offers the obvious solution, with the patient placed 'on-line'. Under the system sketched in Fig. 15 the patient would need only to decide where he wanted to move his hand, and express this desire by contracting some muscle still under his control. The computer would take the myo-electric signal so generated and reapply it as a stimulus to the appropriate joint, again with visual feedback to say when to stop.

We can safely assume that the principles now being developed for powered hands and arms will eventually be applied to legs also. An experimental leg having a hydraulically operated knee joint controlled by myo-electric signals from the thigh has already been developed at the Moscow Institute of Prosthetic Research. This work is backed by careful analysis of the mechanism of walking and the motions of the joints—a surprisingly complex process, as it turns out.

Simpler in many respects is the wheelchair approach to mobility, where man is using a fundamental piece of mechanism unknown in the world of nature. Clumsy and inelegant a prosthesis though the wheelchair is, it can be manufactured simply and cheaply (for less than £20 on the National Health Service). Self-powered versions include an electric one by Scotland's Western Regional Hospital Board for a thalidomide victim who has neither arms nor legs—Britain has a score of these children without hip joints— which the child operates by head movements that initiate the four basic motions of forwards, backwards, left-turn and right-turn.

Another electric wheelchair, developed in Germany, actually climbs stairs, with the help of narrow tracks. Still more sophisticated are the perambulating machines under development by the U.S. aerospace industry for possible use on the Moon, some of the principles of which may translate into simpler 'walking wheelchairs' for the limbless. One obvious handicap, of course, would be the heavy drain on power if machines were used for such manoeuvres as climbing stairs.

ELECTRONIC DETOURS

The blind man tap-tapping his way along the edge of the sidewalk is compensating for his lack of sight by mechanical means. In engineering terms, his cane is a crude 'transducer', sensing the man's position and feeding the appropriate signals to his brain by way of his fingers. But eyes that can see have an immense capacity for conveying information, more than four hundred times greater than even our ears.

Today there are estimated to be 411,000 'legally' blind people in the U.S.A., and another 3·5 million who are only partially sighted. Far more efficient means for bypassing blind eyes are now emerging, the outcome of a better understanding of the physiology, but also of new skills in miniaturizing complex man-made mechanisms.

For example, there are more subtle ways of communicating through the skin than through a stick, or even Braille. Cutaneous communication—'tickle talk'—used with the help of sophisticated instruments is already enabling blind people to 'read' and 'hear' through their fingertips. At Princeton University, for example, Professor Frank Geldard is conducting basic research into cutaneous communication, the interpretation by the skin of patterns of mechanical vibration, in a project sponsored by the Public Health Service and the National Science Foundation. One of his colleagues, Dr Carl E. Sherrick, has devised a vibrotactile transducer that plays an important part in their experiments.[6]

Ten of these transducers placed on fleshy parts of the body, well away from any bones that could short-circuit vibrations to the ear, form the basis of an automatic vibrotactile signalling system, the Optohapt, developed in Geldard's laboratory. A photo-cell converts typed characters into electrical signals, which in turn are changed into mechanical vibrations by the transducers, so to convey their message to the brain by way of the skin.

Another approach has been adopted by Drs Carter Collins and Paul Bach-y-Rita at the Presbyterian Medical Center in San Francisco, who have used a small television camera to feed images to plastic 'needles' presssed against the sensitive skin of the back. Their idea is that thousands of needles might eventually be used to 'tattoo' a pattern. They would drum against the skin without actually piercing it, in a sequence that corresponded to the image 'seen' by the camera. In this way the subject would sense a pattern of light and shade corresponding to his surroundings.

Nevertheless, in referring to tactile communication, as Professor A. M. Uttley pointed out in his opening remarks to the International Conference on Sensory Devices for the Blind, in London in 1966, 'A blind man has in his fingertip something like a six-line picture compared with the 625-line picture of British television. This is again a measure of the restriction we have in trying to get information "in" to the blind person.'[7]

Proceeding on another course, a Mexican psychiatrist has invented a kind of electronic 'eye' that can bypass eyes that have been blinded, feeding its images straight to the brain. Professor Armando del Campo of the National University in Mexico City uses photo-electric cells to do the seeing, and converts their images into electrical impulses that are fed through electrodes fastened just above the eye sockets (see Plate 17) into the trigeminal nerve. The signals thus supplied are not the d.c. signals one would obtain directly from a photo-cell but alternating current, which in some way that is still not understood can provoke the sensation of light and shade in the patient.

Dr del Campo is emphatic that the mechanism is not 'seeing' as we know it, but sensations in black and white, with intermediate tones of grey, generated according to the amount of light an object reflects. The sensations are sufficiently vivid and well defined, he has claimed, to allow his patients to find their way around a room or down a street, and to locate specific objects.

Dr del Campo's empirical approach has achieved a limited measure of success, but more fundamental investigations are taking place in several research centres in the hope of discovering in just what form information is relayed from organs like the eye and the ear to the brain. If these 'codes' — the waveforms of the electrical impulses down the optic and auditory nerves — could be cracked it might be possible to substitute an electronic receptor for a blind eye or deaf ear. But, according to Professors Bernard Saltzberg and Robert Heath of Tulane University School of Medicine, the challengingly difficult problem is to evolve an appropriate code that produces good discrimination in the brain over the vast ensemble of messages that will be presented to the artificial sensory organ.

In short, we want a code that will sift a cogent and unambiguous message from a babble of electronic 'noise'.

Some progress has already been reported by American research teams, such as the differentiation between high and low tones by patients who had lost their hearing. In one study supported by the National Institute of Neurological Diseases and Blindness, the auditory nerve of a sixty-year-old man deaf in both ears was directly stimulated by six micro-electrodes implanted in the nerve, each of which produced a characteristic pitch. The man found he could then recognize gross differences between speech sounds.[8]

Technologically, the problem of microminiaturizing a sensor is no longer formidable. A British laboratory, for example, has recently made an 'opto-electronic' television camera system measuring only 0·4 by 0·14 inch, containing the equivalent of some thousand pounds-worth of TV electronics. It forms the 'eye' of an electronic character-recognizing machine. But a full understanding of the electrical codes will still be crucial to any system that is to come near the information capacity of the living organs.

If we can find ways of simulating man's normal senses there is no reason, in principle, why much the same approach should not equip man with additional senses — the ability to 'see' infra-red or X-rays, or to 'hear' ultra-sound or infra-sound, perhaps, or to 'sense' time or direction instead of reading a watch or compass dial. One can foresee circumstances where the ability instantly to recognize some harmful emanation like radioactivity might be invaluable. In fact research workers with the University of California have so equipped cats that they recognize and react immediately to the presence of radioactivity.

The Scheibels, who report this experiment,[9] make no claim to have cracked the impulse code, and indeed arrived at their code empirically. Their cats are provided with a miniaturized geiger counter strapped to the chest. Each atomic particle the counter registers is turned into a square-wave electrical pulse lasting half a millisecond, a simple imitation of the normal nervous impulses. These pulses are led to selected regions of the cat's brain, through a terminal implanted in the top of its skull. One region they chose to stimulate was the dorso-medial, one which normally reacts to unpleasant sensations. When the cat then approached a small radioactive capsule its 'instinctive' reactions were to crouch, lash its tail and slink off.

The source of the human voice is the larynx, or voice box, of which the vocal cords are a part. Not uncommonly, disease requires the removal of the larynx itself. Then the windpipe, instead of discharging past the vocal cords and into the tortuous cavities of the mouth and throat, which impart the nuances of human speech, is terminated at an artificial opening in the neck. Many who have experienced laryngotomy learn to communicate afresh, by œsophageal speech, a rather indistinct sound but nevertheless an effective means of communication. But about a fifth never master it at all.

Interest in the artificial larynx appears to go back nearly a hundred years, but in 1925 the Bell Telephone Laboratories (whose president had a friend who lost his larynx) began to take an interest in the problem. Early models were mechanical in action, using a diaphragm or reed vibrated by the user's breath, blown through a tube.

Their several disadvantages were greatly ameliorated when, in 1960, Bell Laboratories introduced the electronic counterpart: not unlike the receiver of a telephone, having a vibrating surface that is pressed against the throat when the user wants to talk (see Fig. 16). Harold Barney, in charge of psycho-acoustics research, was responsible for the electronic larynx, which communicates a pattern of sound waves to the throat that can then be shaped into words by the lips, tongue, palate, and so forth.[10]

This battery-powered prosthesis has pitch control over about an octave, with one range for men and a higher one to simulate the female voice. Speech inflection and emphasis can be managed through a thumb-operated on/off and pitch control switch.

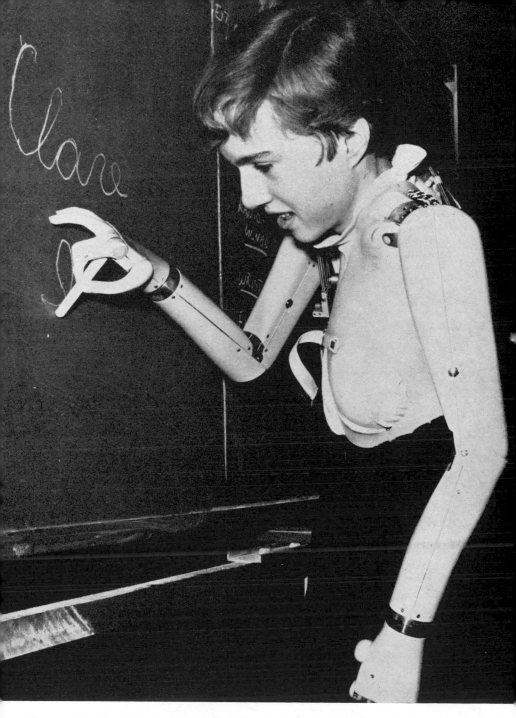

Plate 14. Armless child of fifteen chalks her name with the aid of the hydrauli-cally powered artificial arms, designed by the Northern Electric Research Laboratories, Ottawa

BELL
BUZZ
COMM TEL TYPE
LIGHT TUBE WALL A/P
HEAT OFF SLOW FAST LOW MED HIGH
RADIO OFF T H L
Vol Min 2 3 4 Max
T.V. OFF bbc ITV1 ITV2 ubf?
Vol Min 2 3 4 Max
Brid Min 2 3 4 Max
Con Min 2 3 4 Max
REP N
TAPE OFF HOLD REC3 P.8 REW
E.B. OFF LOW MED High
RESP
INTC OFF ALL NTE DWGR REAR
PRECOM

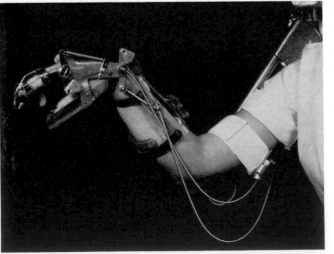

Plate 15. Mr David Hy[e]
tetraplegic since he brok[e]
neck playing Rugby at th[e]
of fifteen, at his P.O.S.M. [opera]tive suite

Plate 16. Orthopaedic brac[e]
seven electrically powered [joints]
controlled through min[iature]
switches operated by the we[arer's]
tongue

Plate 17. The Amauroscope, a Mexican development that uses photo-cells to feed electrical signals to a blind person's brain, allowing him to distinguish hazy patterns of light and shade

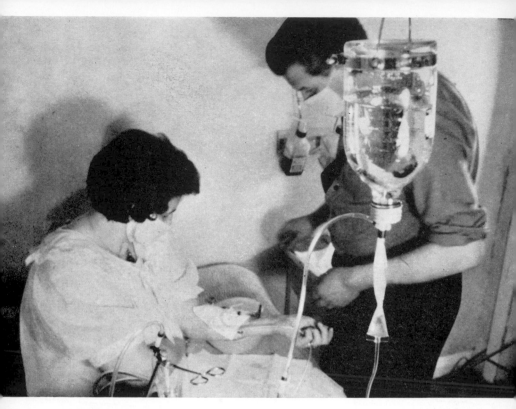

Plates 18 *a* and *b*. Mrs Audrey Worthy, a young London housewife who has her own artificial kidney, being prepared for dialysis by her husband Dennis. (*below*) The artificial kidney and its control console

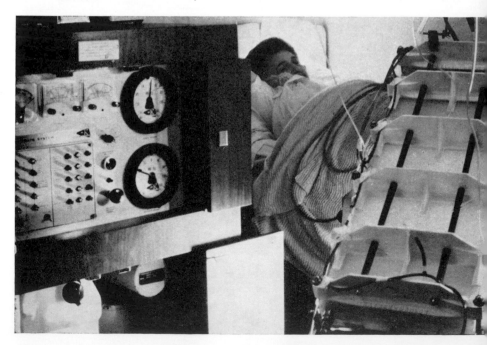

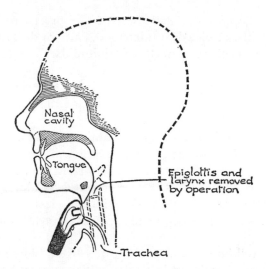

Labels in figure: Nasal cavity, Tongue, Epiglottis and larynx removed by operation, Trachea

Fig. 16. Bell Laboratories' artificial larynx, placed against the neck to transmit its vibration through the skin to the air within the pharynx

Ideally, of course, the artificial larynx would be built into the patient's throat, and in fact a London dental surgeon has designed one into an upper denture. But inevitably there is great difficulty in finding room even for a microminiature version. Power supplies are also a problem. Electrical leads that emerge through the mouth are unhygienic and aesthetically unacceptable.

THE HEART'S PACEMAKER

The heart has an existence of its own. When the surgeon opens up the chest wall and joins his patient's circulatory system to a heart-lung machine that wholly assumes the role of pumping, the heart-beat itself continues unabated. Even a heart that has been completely removed from an animal will continue to beat for some hours, because the tissues of this organ possess what is called an intrinsic rhythmicity. Each individual cell composing the heart beats with its own rhythm.

There is one small region of the right atrium with a particularly high intrinsic rhythmicity, this being a small knot of cells known as the sino-atrial (or sino-auricular: S-A) node. Within the S-A node is generated the impulse that sweeps across the heart, about seventy times a minute, contracting the heart muscle and so

G

expelling the blood contained therein. The precise nature of this stimulus is still not clearly understood, but we do know that at some point it becomes an electrical impulse, the E.C.G. This electrical impulse can reach the ventricles (in the lower half of the heart) only by way of a narrow bridge of electrically conducting cells. Should these cells become diseased the patient is said to be suffering from 'heart block'.

As such, heart block is not a fatal condition, because the intrinsic rhythmicity of the cardiac muscle will keep the ventricles pulsating, albeit at their own, often very slow rate. So the patient becomes incapacitated. In the case of a Stokes-Adams syndrome, the heart rate becomes very slow indeed, less than twenty a minute, and the patient begins to show all the symptoms of 'heart failure'.

It is now well known that a sharp jolt like a blow on the chest can often persuade a heart in this condition to start beating more vigorously. For many years chemical stimulants such as epiphrine, sometimes injected straight into the heart muscle, have been used for the same purpose.

However, in 1950, Dr Paul Zoll of the Harvard Medical School tried another method. He attempted to apply an electric stimulus across the chest of a dying man of seventy-five who had failed to respond to chemical stimulants. Powerful shocks overrode the S-A node to revive the patient briefly, but his heart by this time was too badly damaged. A month later Dr Zoll tried again with another patient, and this time he lived. It was fifty-two hours before his heart responded to the electrical jolts and regained its own rhythmicity, but thereafter the patient lived for eight months without further help for his heart.

The technique is now an established one in hospitals. An apparatus known as a defibrillator is used to discharge 2,000 or 3,000 volts across an asynchronous heart.

But several surgeons had begun to investigate the possibility of providing a faltering heart with a more permanent electrical stimulus. Applied externally, across the high electrical resistance of the skin, the electrical requirements are heavy and cause painful contractions of the chest muscles, and even burns. But when applied to the heart itself they seemed much more modest; merely microwatts at a few volts to provide the low-frequency impulses, seventy or so a minute. Moreover the transistor, invented in 1947, was emerging as the ideal component around which to build a diminutive stimulator—small, reliable, and modest in its need of power.

In 1957 a Minnesotan heart surgeon, Dr C. Walton Lillehei, abetted by two electronic engineers, produced the counterpart of today's artificial kidney. It was an electronic 'pacemaker' into which the patient could be plugged by way of silver-plated wires that passed through the chest wall and were stitched to the surface of the heart itself. Dr Lillehei made the first clinical application on January 30th, 1957, and reported that 'control of the heartbeat was obtained easily with voltages of 0·8 to 9·0'.[11]

The next step was to miniaturize the electronics to the point where they might be implanted into the body, permanently if necessary, to augment the beat of the physiological pacemaker. A Swede, Dr Ake Senning, succeeded first, closely followed by a number of American surgeons, among them the surgeon-engineer team of Dr William Chardack and Wilson Greatbatch, with its five-ounce, battery-powered package.

Merely to provide an instrument that jolts the heart into action, however, is a fairly crude approach to helping a patient. For one thing it soon becomes apparent that too powerful a shock will damage the heart muscle around the electrodes. At the same time, if the device is to be permanently implanted there is every incentive to use as little power as possible. The minimum requirements, it turns out, are a pulse lasting up to two-thousandths of a second, drawing from two to seven milliamps of current, which requires about six volts to overcome the electrical resistance of the heart.

The surgeons had to discover the best point at which to apply the pulse and initially the technique was to sew the electrodes to the surface of the lower half of the heart. But the surgical technique proved too much of a strain for many elderly heart patients, and a refinement emerged in which the stimulus is applied to the right ventricle by way of an insulated wire that is passed along a vein into the heart. The platinum tip of this wire is carefully attached in the apex of the right ventricle; the point of attachment, which is followed by X-radiography, being critical.

The surgical technique of equipping heart patients with an electronic pacemaker has developed astonishingly quickly, and in

99

the U.S. there are over 25,000 people who owe their well-being today to an electronic package about the size of a cigarette packet. The device moreover is not simply a last desperate resort for elderly victims of heart disease. In January 1967 *The Times* reported that 'Mrs Valerie Marsden, aged twenty-one, whose heart is kept going by a battery, has given birth to a seven-pound baby at Hull Maternity Hospital.'

But the technique is by no means fully developed. For one thing, it may not be easy to find a place in which to bury the pacemaker itself, which can both accommodate its volume comfortably and securely and allow fairly ready access for replacement of the batteries. In a woman it can be implanted beneath a breast, and in a well-built man under the armpit; but a thin man may more conveniently be provided with an external pacemaker.

Nor is a simple instrument delivering an unvarying seventy pulses a minute necessarily the last word, for the healthy heart responds immediately to all manner of external stimuli, from physical exertion to sensual excitement, and a similar response to physiological demands should certainly be advantageous. E. F. Adolph, writing in the *Scientific American*, holds that the best solution 'would be the implantation of living pacemaker tissue from a human donor or an animal one ... Unfortunately in mammals implanted tissue does not wed itself to the heart but simply forms a scar.'[12]

One early pacemaker was in fact adjustable—by means of a needle that pierced the patient's skin to act as a screwdriver, so to vary the frequency of the impulses! More subtle is the so-called synchronous pacemaker which, instead of simply overriding the S-A node, takes its cue from the electrical impulses of the auricle; these are picked up by an extra electrode in the atrial wall. These natural impulses are then used to synchronize the pumping rates of the atria and the ventricles, with the pacemaker in effect behaving as an artificial neuron, electrically reconnecting the low- and high-pressure halves of the heart.

The first implantable pacemaker was driven by a miniature accumulator; twin nickel-cadmium cells that could be recharged once a month, overnight, by high-frequency electromagnetic waves beamed through the skin. The accumulator itself, unfortunately, proved none too reliable, and the system was soon supplanted by the mercury battery, a button-sized cell of the kind used to run an electric watch and other miniaturized instruments, that we met in Chapter 1. It has the special feature of sustaining its voltage until very near the end of its life. What is more, the user is warned that its life is nearing an end by a change in the pacemaker's frequency; a warning that can be confirmed by X-rays, for a spent cell is clearly distinguishable from a new one.

The mercury battery is manufactured to exceptionally high standards of quality and reliability, from very carefully chosen materials, for medical use.[13] These so-called 'certified cells' are designed for a continuous service at 37 °C under an average current drain of twenty microamperes.

Theoretically, these minuscule mercury batteries should last for four to five years, but in practice they fall somewhat short, two or three years. Up till now this has not been the major worry; or rather, it has been disguised by other technical difficulties such as broken leads, fatigued by the incessant motions of living tissues, the failure of other components, and seepage of body fluids into the pacemaker. As the technology of the pacemaker improves, however, its power supply, even though replaceable under a local anaesthetic nowadays, will loom large as a limitation.

There are alternatives, some of which are examined in the next chapter as potential sources of power for an artificial organ. The difference is, of course, that a pacemaker needs much less power, microwatts rather than watts. One very attractive prospect at the moment is the radiation from a radioisotope, which can be used to heat a thermocouple, so creating a small flow of current. The scheme is already used in other inaccessible situations—to provide power to Dungeness lighthouse, for example.

The difficulty of this approach, of course, is that living cells are extremely sensitive to radiation—more is said about this in the discussion on transplanted tissue in Chapter V—and the radio-active capsule must be meticulously shielded. Fig. 17 shows the pacemaker, with its built-in nuclear powerpack, that is being developed by the Nuclear Materials and Equipment Corporation of Apollo, Pennsylvania, for the U.S. Atomic Energy Commission. The specification calls for a pacemaker with a life of at least 10 years, that will administer pulses lasting 1·5 milliseconds at the rate of 70 a minute; and which will not expose the wearer to a

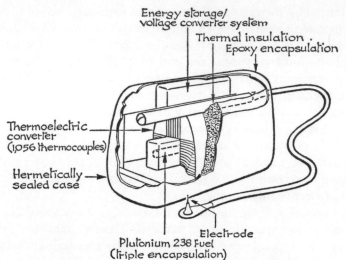

Energy storage/
voltage converter system

Thermal insulation .
Epoxy encapsulation

Thermoelectric
converter
(1,056 thermocouples)

Hermetically
sealed case

Plutonium 238 fuel
(triple encapsulation)

Electrode

FIG. 17. Heart pacemaker with a built-in source of power. Alpha radiation from a radioisotope, plutonium-238, will heat thermo-electric couples to provide adequate power for at least ten years

temperature rise of more than 3 °F or a radiation level higher than 5 millirems an hour. British scientists are developing a similar pacemaker.

There are heart conditions that cause the heart to race at an alarming rate, 200 or more a minute, that also gravely impair its efficiency as a blood pump. To correct this situation another kind of pacemaker, the so-called 'paired-pulse' type, has been developed in recent years. The idea is that the first pulse of a pair shall initiate contraction; while the second, which follows after a carefully chosen interval, is used to block the heart's response to the next natural stimulus. One team has reported on a man whose heart rate of up to 200 was steadied to 70 in this way.[14]

Other failing muscles besides those of the heart can be stimulated to order by electrical shocks. One of the most serious complications of paralysis, for example, is an infected bladder or urinary tract, a consequence of the retention of urine and the bacteria it contains. This problem is still responsible for more than half the deaths among the paralysed. The answer could lie with an electrical 'pacemaker' that artificially stimulates the bladder to contract, as it were, upon demand.

Such a device has been developed by two surgeons with the

Maimonides Hospital of Brooklyn, New York, working in collaboration with the Avco-Everett Research Laboratory. It is called a 'radio physiologic' stimulator, the invention of Dr Adrian Kantrowitz and Dr Martin Schamaun. The bladder (detrusor) muscle is stimulated by the application of a train of electrical pulses to electrodes affixed front and back.[15] These stainless steel electrodes are fed with low-voltage impulses from a small radio receiver, just over an inch across, buried in a pocket beneath the skin of the patient's stomach. At the touch of a button on the torch-like radio transmitter, the paralysed person can contract his own bladder, so causing it to empty (see Fig. 18).

It may even be possible to relieve some kinds of severe pain by an electrical stimulator of this kind, as medical scientists with the National Heart Institute in Bethesda, Maryland, indicated early in 1968, when they reported success in controlling the acutely distressing pain of angina pectoris. Their stimulator acts upon the carotid sinus nerves in the neck, that control blood pressure. Electrical pulses override the normal control of these nerves,

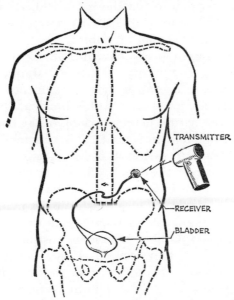

FIG. 18. The Avco radio-physiologic stimulator attached to the bladder. Stainless steel electrodes implanted in the detrusor muscles convey an electrical signal that contracts the muscles and empties the bladder

keeping the heart rate and blood pressure high, so avoiding the blood starvation of the heart muscle that causes the pain.

SPINAL MAN

Physiology rather than electronics is the key to a quite different method of bypassing a fault in bodily function, and nowhere is this better illustrated than in the rehabilitation of those people who are paralysed through disease or injury of the spinal cord.

The brain itself is actually an extension of this cord: the central cable of the body's nervous system; a bundle of nerve tissue extending downwards for eighteen to twenty inches from the base of the brain. From this cord radiate thirty-one pairs of nerves. controlling every part of the body other than the head itself, Injury to the spinal cord, then, is almost certain to have serious consequences. Today it depends importantly on how high up the cord the injury occurs, for the higher the lesion the greater the number of nerves cut off from the brain.

A quarter of a century ago the likely consequence of severing the cord in an accident or on the battlefield, for example, or of the destruction of some of its cells by a disease such as polio-myelitis, was a life of virtual immobility.

Engineers in recent years have begun to worry about the rapidly increasing complexity of their creations, and the con-sequences of failure in only a few components. Today, a big electronic telephone exchange—which incidentally has much in common with the central nervous system of the body—may have more than a million components. The engineer's solution to failure difficulties is to design into his systems something called 'built-in redundancy'—the capacity for the machine automatically to bypass many kinds of faults by using circuits and mechanisms that normally lie dormant, or are used at less than full capacity.

The latest developments in microminiature electronics afford tremendous scope for built-in redundancy without any significant increase in the volume they occupy. Many of the systems used, for example, in modern weapons and spacecraft, or in an aircraft's blind-landing apparatus, where the utmost reliability is expected (one failure in 10 million landings is the goal of the aircraft blind-landing systems being developed in Britain), now duplicate and even triplicate many parts of the system.

104

Man, nature's most complex mechanism, and one far more complicated than anything man has thought seriously of making, has a built-in redundancy we have scarcely begun to explore. Doctors are just beginning to appreciate the capacity of the brain in this respect. To quote a leading article in the *Lancet*, ' ... children in particular have remarkable powers of recovery, probably because the brain is still more or less multipotential and one area can compensate for the loss of another ... '[16] But in one area where this capacity has been explored systematically surgeons have already succeeded in rehabilitating many thousands of patients. This is the treatment of spinal injuries—of 'spinal man', as he is called.

In 1943 the British Government set up a Spinal Injuries Unit at the military hospital at Stoke Mandeville in Buckinghamshire, and to this unit the following year came Dr Ludwig Guttmann, a physiologist with revolutionary ideas for the treatment of the paralysed victims of war. This fierce little man, full of energy and dedication, soon to earn from his patients the sobriquet of 'Poppa', immediately confounded his critics by achieving the most amazing mobility in patients who previously would have been condemned to spend the few remaining years of their lives—ten years was the maximum the paraplegic or person paralysed in the lower limbs could expect to live—on their backs.

Accepting the premise that there could be no rejoining of a spinal cord severed by injury or disease, Dr Guttmann looked elsewhere for the muscle power to activate those portions of the body rendered useless by the trauma, so to bypass the isolated length of cord. The principles he enunciated and began to employ at Stoke Mandeville over twenty-five years ago are now practised throughout the world.

Perhaps his most powerful ally in the rehabilitation of spinal man is the *latissimus dorsi*—'wide muscle across the back', as its name indicates. This is the muscle which adducts and rotates the arm, for which purpose the muscle braces itself against the big bone of the pelvis. If this mechanism is put into reverse, by bracing the other end of the *latissimus dorsi*, the one which normally contracts, this muscle can be used instead to swing the pelvis. A child does this when 'walking' on stilts, by gripping the top of the stilts. A paraplegic (who still retains the use of his arms) can do the same by bracing his arms against parallel bars or elbow crutches.

Latissimus dorsi can be assisted in restoring an upright posture by another large back muscle, the *trapezius*. This muscle is attached to the lowest vertebrae, and the two together can form a 'physiological corset' that enables spinal man to keep his equilibrium when sitting or standing.

Between them, these two muscles can confer upon spinal man the ability both to stand erect and to swing the pelvis. But the muscles of his thighs are also anchored to his pelvis, and these muscles in turn act upon those of the legs and, through them, the feet. Once spinal man has learned to use his pelvis in this way he begins to regain control of other paralysed muscles.

In all patients with a break in their spinal cord above the twelfth dorsal segment, one major complication arises: they lose all sense of their position in space; in other words, they no longer have any awareness of balance. This awareness must be inculcated anew, by using the eyes to provide 'feedback' of information whilst the patient is learning to stand and walk again. Mirrors tell him when he is keeling over, until he has re-learnt his sense of balance.

Inevitably there are many other complications facing spinal man, and a great deal will depend upon the severity of his injury, for as we know, the higher up the cord is severed, the more extensive the paralysis, and the more difficult it is to find dormant muscle power to harness. If the injury is as high as the cervical nerves, for example, the muscles of the arms themselves may be paralysed, a condition known as tetraplegia (or quadraplegia). Muscular control of the diaphragm may also be interrupted, so that the patient will need permanent artificial respiration.

By a strict regime of physiotherapy, Dr (now Sir Ludwig) Guttmann has persuaded many hopelessly crippled people to become self-sufficient. Although they never discard the wheelchair, they usually return to a surprisingly normal domestic and workaday life, after an average span of only about 20 weeks in hospital. Many marry and even an active sex life may be restored, the result of a discovery that injections of the drug prostigmine, given to control the spasms that frequently afflict paralysed muscles, can cause a patient to ejaculate. A member of his staff, recounting the discovery, tells how Guttmann 'grabbed a bottle and dashed off to the lab to examine the precious fluid.

He came back in about twenty minutes, shook the patient warmly by the hand, saying, "Congratulations, you can have a baby." '

The factor that limits the extent of the patient's recovery is no longer the severity of the injury itself but largely the personality and attitude of the patient—'the most important member of the rehabilitation team', according to Dr Guttmann.

Sport provides an incentive as well as the discipline for the lengthy rehabilitation period. Having introduced his earliest patients at Stoke Mandeville to the throwing of medicine balls and later to archery, Dr Guttmann in 1948 founded the International Stoke Mandeville Games for the Paralysed—the 'Paralympics'. These are now held every four years, immediately following the Olympic Games.

These wheelchair athletes have recorded some astonishing feats: a javelin thrown 34 metres and a shot-put of 10·44 metres, for example; a weight of 200 kilograms lifted from a lying position, and a discus hurled 36·98 metres.

THE ARTIFICIAL KIDNEY

'The main functions of the kidneys,' Professor Hugh de Wardener of Charing Cross Hospital told a conference in London in 1966, 'are to keep the electrolyte and water content of the body within constant limits and to eliminate certain waste products of protein metabolism. If the patient has not sufficient renal function to do these things he will die. Life can be maintained however by circulating the patient's blood from time to time through an artificial kidney, even if both the patient's kidneys have been totally destroyed or removed. This is the manoeuvre that is known as haemodialysis.'

Thousands of people die every year from kidney failure, through accident, disease, damage, poisoning or 'shock'. It is well over fifty years since the first attempt was made, in the U.S.A., to replace the kidneys' dual function of filter and body fluid balancer with an artificial piece of chemical engineering. This was by Abel, Rowntree and Turner, whose 'dialyser' still exists in a laboratory of the Cornell University College of Medicine. It failed because its inventors lacked a satisfactory filter and a way to prevent the bypassed blood from clotting.

The first artificial kidney to work was the clandestine invention of a Dutch surgeon, Willem J. Kolff, in a small hospital at Kampen. Helped by a local manufacturer, H. T. J. Berk, he defied the wartime Nazi occupation of his country to develop a system that used Cellophane (cellulose acetate film) as the filter membrane and heparin as the anticoagulant. Kolff wound a long tube of Cellophane around a drum, which he then set rotating in a tankful of brine.

Ironically, his first success was with a Nazi collaborator. His patient's blood was forced, by her heart and under the pull of gravity, through several yards of coiled Cellophane tube. In its long passage the impurities that had accumulated in the blood passed across the 'semi-permeable' membrane into the brine beyond; and certain constituents of the brine including salt (sodium chloride) and glucose passed in the opposite direction to replenish the blood. Through keeping the concentration of the brine close to that of blood in respect of certain salts, no loss of these salts took place from the bloodstream.

The process was simply filtration, but of molecules not particles of matter. Those substances the kidneys are intended to remove are mostly of fairly small molecular weight, urea and creatinine for instance, and pass readily through the pores of a Cellophane membrane.

Dialysis, as this process of molecular filtration is known—it comes from the Greek for 'separation'—is the principle behind every successful artificial kidney so far. Kolff, for example, who emigrated to the U.S.A. after the war, saw his filter developed into two different commercial versions, and himself made another important contribution to its progress when around 1956 he developed the disposable membrane unit. Other artificial kidneys were emerging, among them an engineered version of a kidney invented by another European surgeon, Dr Frederick Kiil, in Norway, again during the German wartime occupation.

But despite the essential simplicity of the process, and its obvious success, haemodialysis was to remain no more than an emergency treatment, for cases where the kidneys had failed abruptly but were thought to stand a chance of regaining their normal function. The reason was quite simple: the patient had to be permanently 'plugged into' a large and cumbersome piece of apparatus, through which his blood was kept circulating.

In fact, there is no need for the treatment to be continuous. Intermittent dialysis for a few hours a week is sufficient to keep the blood in balance and the patient reasonably healthy. What was lacking was a convenient way of connecting and disconnecting the patient, which would avoid the need to cut into a major blood vessel each time; for even if the surgery were acceptable the surgeon would soon run out of fresh sites into which to join the artificial kidney.

It meant, of course, that anyone suffering from chronic renal failure, whose kidneys would never work again, was condemned to a most unpleasant death.

Salvation lay with a team led by Dr Belding H. Scribner at the University of Washington School of Medicine in Seattle, who in 1962 first demonstrated the Scribner shunt, a 'socket' permanently implanted in the circulatory system, between an artery and a vein, that can rapidly be opened and joined to the artificial kidney. The clue to its success lay more than anything in the choice of materials that are not rejected by the body, which was made by Wayne Quinton, the engineer in the team.[17]

This shunt is a tube of silicone rubber, a material we shall meet again in Chapter 4, tipped with Teflon (polytetrafluoroethylene), another extremely unreactive plastic. It is U-shaped and some six inches in length, with ends that penetrate the skin to be stitched securely in place in an adjoining artery and vein, usually in the forearm or just above the ankle (see Plate 18). Metal clips, secured to the skin with plaster, are often used to anchor the shunt.

Various refinements of the Scribner shunt have since been advanced, but the original version is still widely used and usually causes the patient remarkably little discomfort, considering the risk of any percutaneous (skin-piercing) connection of this kind. When not in use it must be kept covered and dry, but otherwise causes its wearer little inconvenience. If it should become infected it is shifted to a fresh site.

The Scribner shunt—an inexpensive device: it now costs only about a pound—liberated the artificial kidney from its role as the tool of research and emergency. Today hundreds of people, many quite young, lead virtually normal lives, interrupted only by the need to spend two or three nights a week coupled to a machine.

Even their diet is reasonably normal, restricted chiefly by the need to avoid foods that contain a lot of potassium, like ice-cream, nuts and chocolate. Regular dialysis is advised, but as patients grow more accustomed to their machines they are finding that they can go for several days—five or six at least—without discomfort; long enough to enjoy a short holiday.

'I cried when I first saw the "kidney" and thought of all that trouble,' Mrs Audrey Worthy, a plump young London housewife, told me, 'but now it's child's play.' A few years ago she nearly died, before coming under the charge of Dr Stanley Shaldon, one of Britain's pioneers in treatment with the artificial kidney, at the Royal Free Hospital in London.

Restored to health she became in 1965 one of the first patients in the world to be provided with her own artificial kidney, for self-treatment at home. The early days were turbulent ones, for life with a machine can impose a tremendous emotional stress—some marriages have come asunder here—but today Mrs Worthy and her husband are totally reconciled to living with their complex life preserver. Their only real contact with the Royal Free's kidney unit is by phone, with a bi-monthly visit to pick up fresh supplies of dialysate. Other home kidney patients of this hospital live as far away as Jordan, Switzerland and Aden (although most are within a few miles), and Dennis Worthy dreams of a European holiday 'club', with patients using each other's dialysers and their own portable kidneys.

But the emancipation of the artificial kidney brought problems galore. Designed principally by medical men, these programmed filter pumps were cumbersome and costly to run and to service, constantly demanding expert attention, medical as well as technical; designed in fact for relatively short periods of continuous use. Quite different were the requirements of a machine that must serve many patients in rapid succession, as in the units for chronic renal failure that many hospitals have acquired in the last five years. Still other characteristics are sought in a machine to be installed in the patient's own home, or one trundled from door to door in an ambulance.

One of the most reliable and foolproof machines for haemodialysis, and the one on which a very large proportion of the clinical experience with chronic renal failure in the U.S.A. and

Britain has been amassed, is a highly developed version of Kiil's kidney. It has been engineered by the Milton-Roy Company of St Petersburgh, Florida, a firm specializing in the fluid control of chemical processes.[18] This is the kidney on which both Dr Scribner in the U.S.A. and Dr Shaldon in Britain based their pioneering experiments in home dialysis.

The kidney of the Kiil-Roy haemodialyzer is nothing more than two sheets of Cellophane sandwiched between boards of polypropylene. The patient's blood flows from the shunt to fill the volume between the membranes, while the arm 'dialysate' or washing brine flows over their outer surfaces and down the drain. The unwanted constituents of the blood, including much of its water content, find their way through the membranes, while salt, glucose and other constituents of the dialysate replenish the blood.

This very simple filter press is served by a most elaborate array of controls (see Fig. 19) that monitor the temperature and conductivity of the dialysate, the negative pressure within the kidney (to sense a blockage), and the contents of the spent dialysate (to detect any trace of blood that has found its way through a perforated membrane). On a cold night the machine can be set to dialyse at a slightly higher temperature. If anything at all should go awry the machine emits a piercing shriek that cannot be ignored.

Then, after the allotted period of dialysis—two sessions of fourteen hours or three of ten hours a week are most commonly adopted—the patient is weighed, and the dialysing process adjusted to rapidly remove any excess of fluid that may have accumulated. A bed that automatically registers any change in the patient's weight is normally used. Once the patient has been disconnected the final task is to sterilize the apparatus, an automatic thirty-minute process that leaves everything ready for the next dialysis.

Likewise, Kolff's coiled membrane system has been engineered into a reliable equipment, by the Travenol Laboratories of Morton Grove, Illinois. The kidney in this case consists of a twin coil that is quickly inserted into the apparatus, where it is immersed in a large volume of dialysate. The patient's blood is pumped into the centre of the coils, to emerge at the periphery having traversed some sixteen feet of Cellophane tubing. The coils themselves,

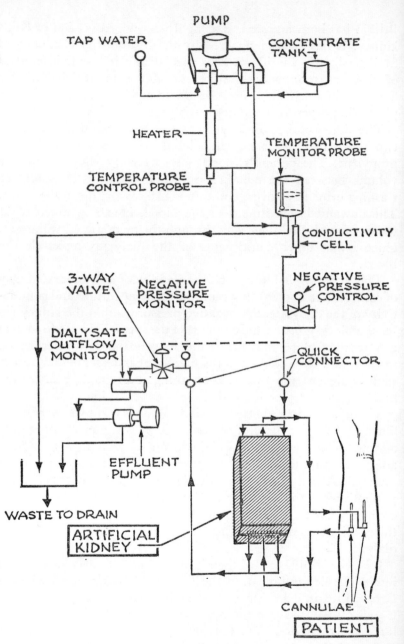

PUMP

TAP WATER

CONCENTRATE TANK

HEATER

TEMPERATURE MONITOR PROBE

TEMPERATURE CONTROL PROBE

CONDUCTIVITY CELL

3-WAY VALVE

NEGATIVE PRESSURE MONITOR

NEGATIVE PRESSURE CONTROL

DIALYSATE OUTFLOW MONITOR

QUICK CONNECTOR

EFFLUENT PUMP

WASTE TO DRAIN

ARTIFICIAL KIDNEY

CANNULAE

PATIENT

Fig. 19. Flow circuit for the Milton-Roy home haemodialysis unit, designed as a foolproof system to operate without skilled supervision

112

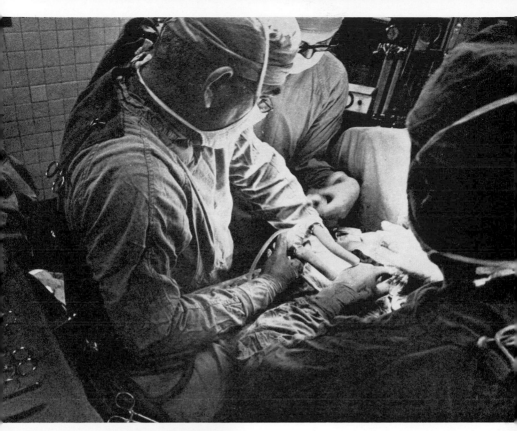

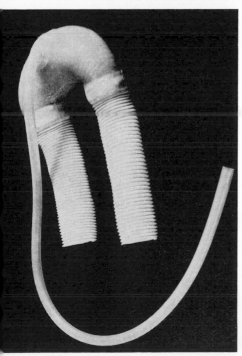

Plates 19 *a* and *b*. Dr Adrian Kantrowitz, a New York surgeon, with the mechanical auxiliary ventricle or 'booster' heart developed with his brother, Dr Arthur Kantrowitz of the Avco Corporation. The silicone booster heart is shown (*left*)

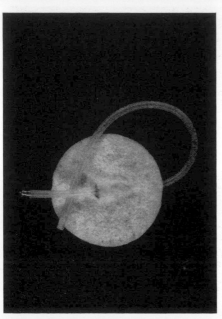

Plate 20. (*left*) Percutaneous power connection developed at the University of Pennsylvania. It is implanted in two stages. First the connection is buried beneath the skin, with the lead extending to the organ itself. Then, once accepted the skin is punctured and the tube withdrawn

Plate 21. (*below*) Pacemaker powered by a 'biological battery', using electrodes of zinc and platinum black, developed by Canada's National Research Council. It can draw up to 300 microwatts from living tissues

Plate 22. (*facing page, top*) Piezoelectric generator that draws its power from aortic pulsations

Plate 23. (*facing page, bottom*) Testing the strength of a silicone bonding agent applied between a porcelain tooth and a resin rod, at the National Bureau of Standards, in quest of one that gives stronger dentures and prevents seepage of food and bacteria between the teeth and the denture bases

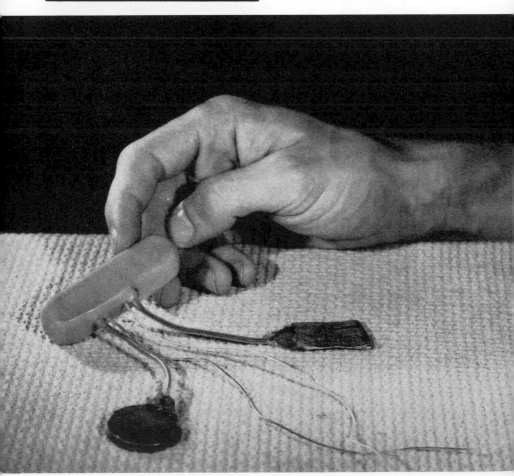

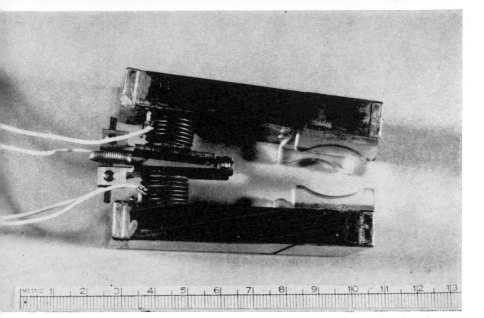

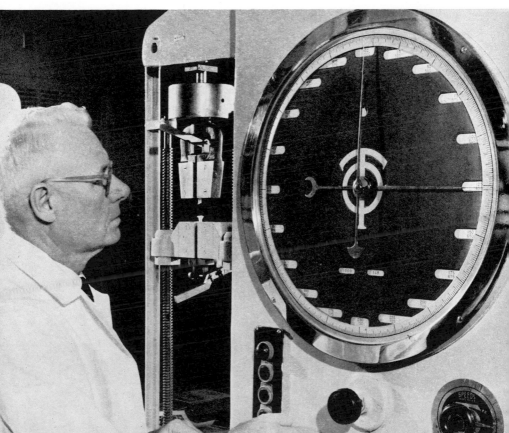

Plate 24. Prototype of an artificial heart of silicone rubber, developed in the laboratories of the Goodyear Tire and Rubber Company. This air-driven prosthesis has been developed in collaboration with Dr Willem Kolff

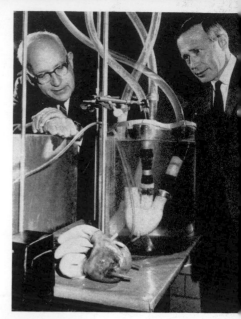

Plate 25. Starr-Edwards ball valve about to be sutured into a heart

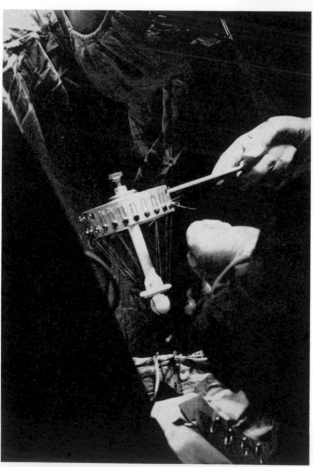

supplied sterile and ready for immediate use, are disposable and can be changed in a few minutes—one important advantage claimed for this system.

Quite a different membrane structure is used in the Dow hollow-fibre kidney, where about 11,000 fibres of cellulose, anchored in silicone resin, are bundled together to make a very compact cylindrical filter about fifteen centimetres in length. The patient's blood flows along these slender fibres, only twice the thickness of human hair, while dialysate circulates between them. Once in production the hollow-fibre kidney is expected to be cheap and disposable.

No urologist is under any illusion, however, that the ultimate has been reached, or indeed approached, in the design of artificial kidneys. To quote the late Dr Peter F. Salisbury, at a conference in Cleveland, Ohio, in 1964, 'If the hard facts about the artificial kidney are compared to the area of Manhattan, the unknown parameters would loom as large as our continent.'

He went on to indicate how incredibly fortuitous it is that the artificial kidney as we know it today should work at all. It is one thing for a machine to purge the body of an overdose of some chemical, or to sustain it through a temporary lapse of kidney function, but quite another to regulate the composition of the blood and other body fluids, both within and outside individual cells, so that the body's metabolic processes may continue under optimal conditions. Yet the fact that so many gravely sick patients not only survive but are restored to a state of health where the major operation of kidney transplantation may be considered with equanimity (see Chapter 5) testifies to its enormous success.

Nevertheless, there is plenty of room to improve even present-day artificial kidneys, notably in the areas of reducing their size and cost, improving the speed of the process, and reducing such risks as blood clotting and infection. One improvement that could contribute to several of these areas is a more efficient membrane, now sought by many research teams. Just how Cellophane and similar membranes work is still not fully explained; no electron microscope has even revealed the holes through which the dialysing molecules must pass. This quest, also pursued for its promise as a method of separating the salt from seawater, could lead to more selective membranes, for the more specific treatment of a patient, especially in cases of poisoning, and to a much more compact type of kidney.

One way of improving the efficiency of the process and so reducing the size of the kidney could be to use the closely related process of electro-dialysis, in which the transfer of salts is accelerated by an electric current. Such a kidney was developed in Japan a few years ago, by Professor Takeshi Minami of Jikei University School of Medicine in Tokyo.

The Jikei electro-dialyser uses Cellophane membranes, but the kidney is much smaller than the Kiil kidney and needs only four or five litres of dialysate. It draws four to five amps at twenty to thirty volts d.c. Electro-dialysis also shows promise as a method of separating the salts from salty water, as does another, involving bundles of semi-permeable capillary tubes, capable of providing a large filter area in a small volume. From this closely related technique of desalination we may expect important progress in kidney development.

But the breakthrough to a very much smaller kind of kidney, showing real prospects of being implantable or nearly so, will probably have to come from some quite different mechanism of sifting the body's impurities, such as their absorption by a solid substance. A Greek research worker, for example, has shown that all impurities but urea (in small amounts only) are adsorbed by

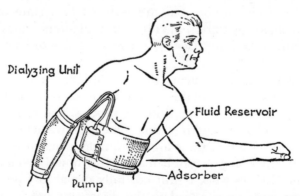

FIG. 20. Artist's sketch of a possible artificial kidney of the future, employing adsorption of the blood's impurities on activated charcoal

activated charcoal—without harm to the blood. An American team has already taken the idea of charcoal adsorption to the stage of visualizing a wearable artificial kidney. Ted Blaney and his colleagues, describing their 'step towards a wearable artificial kidney' to the American Society for Artificial Internal Organs in 1966, pictured the wearer with a dialysing unit encircling one arm and a fluid reservoir containing particles of carbon around his waist (see Fig. 20).

Whether this contrivance would be more acceptable than the intermittent dialysis that allows Audrey Worthy to garden, play bingo, dance and go on holiday, encumbered only by a few centimetres of tubing implanted in her wrist, is doubtful. But it would be an enormous step nearer an implantable kidney to match the artificial hearts discussed in the next chapter of this book.

THE ARTIFICIAL LUNG

The lung, like the kidney, is essentially mechanical in action and so appears an attractive prospect for replacement by a prosthesis. A further inducement is that, unlike the heart, the lung is not self-powered but inflates under atmospheric pressure, in response to an increase in the volume of the chest cavity. The lungs simply expand to fill the space available. (A distinction must be drawn here between the artificial lung, essentially a membrane exposed on one side to blood and the other to the atmosphere, and the 'iron lung' or respirator and its more recent refinements, employed when the patient's chest muscles are paralysed and he can no longer inflate his own lungs.)

The major technical difficulty in attempting to imitate the lung itself is that of providing a membrane roughly the area of a tennis court, of remarkably high permeability to oxygen and carbon dioxide, within the volume of the thorax.

A theoretical scheme for an artificial lung was described to the American Society for Artificial Internal Organs in 1966 by Dr E. Converse Peirce II of Emory University, Atlanta. It is sketched in Fig. 21. The membrane is of silicone, only one-thousandth of an inch thick and a square metre in total area. Concentric layers of this membrane would be kept apart and self-supported by a pattern of points embossed upon it, forming channels between

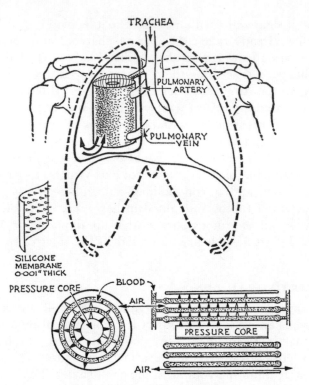

FIG. 21. Artist's sketch of a possible implantable artificial
lung of the future, using coils of a semi-permeable silicone
membrane

only 0·5 millimetre in diameter and 0·1 millimetre high, to
serve as blood capillaries. The very high rate of throughput of
blood, compared with the natural lung, is intended to compensate
for a far smaller surface area.

Thin silicone films allow oxygen and carbon dioxide to diffuse
through them very rapidly indeed — about a hundred times as
fast as any other kind of film. Not the least of the problems,
however, is to prevent the silicone membrane from becoming
choked by coagulated blood over a long period. It is likely that a
membrane with a built-in anticoagulant would be needed for the
role of an implantable 'lung'.

Meanwhile, these silicone films are likely to find their first
application in heart-lung machines used in operating theatres,

for open-heart surgery, in oxygenators for the preservation of live organs such as kidneys, and perhaps within five years or so in artificial 'gills' that will permit a diver to breathe the oxygen dissolved in water.

CHAPTER FOUR

Man Mimicked

'The chemists would like to be able to synthesize natural protein as well as to make different kinds of protein, and we're getting close ... '

Professor Charles C. Price

IT IS hard to assess whether an artificial lung or kidney compact enough to be implanted, that will mimic rather than merely augment the performance of the natural organ, will ever be successful. But the organ that surgeons are making the most determined attempt to mimic is the heart.

The heart, popularly held to be the seat of human emotion — the heart has its reasons of which reason knows nothing, wrote Pascal in *Pensées* — is more accurately viewed in the simpler role of blood pump: three-quarters of a pound of muscle, expelling two or three ounces of blood at a time, around seventy times a minute, to irrigate some 60,000 miles of blood vessels. The simplicity, however, is purely relative, for upon closer inspection this organ appears quite astonishingly complex in its performance. As its action is predominantly mechanical, however, and since over a million citizens of the world's most affluent nation die every year from 'heart failure' of one kind or another, the urge to mimic its performance is at least understandable.

The truly artificial heart is the great prestige goal of American medical science today: a project set in train around 1957 by the late Dr Peter Salisbury, founder of the American Society for Artificial Internal Organs. Its lessons and techniques are helping to shape the entire field of prosthetic research, and for this reason alone the quest for an implantable heart is worth examining in some detail.

Frank W. Hastings, who heads the artificial heart programme of the National Heart Institute in Bethesda, has pointed out that several different kinds of artificial heart will probably be needed: 'First, there is a need for a temporary-assist device that is simple to use, safe, and effective. Hopefully its installation will not require major surgery. Second, there is probably a need for a permanent-assist device which will eventually be totally implantable. Third, a total heart replacement will be needed for patients with hearts damaged beyond salvage, which must take over the entire function of the natural heart. Lastly, there is a need for an emergency system which would increase the number of heart-attack patients surviving to reach hospital.'

Let us examine the first three kinds of artificial heart foreseen by Dr Hastings (the fourth machine does not concern us here).

Chapter 1 has provided some impression of the complexity and sensitivity of the fluid the heart must handle: no ordinary liquid, but a delicate balance of living cells and saline fluid; a living tissue, virtually an organ in its own right, whose responsibility it is to keep all the other tissues of the body supplied with nutrients. Deprived of these nutrients, parts of the brain tissue, for example, begin to die in a matter of minutes.

The first problem, then, is to find a way of handling this fluid without in any way altering its nature: a remarkably difficult problem, as it turns out, for blood is very easily perturbed by most kinds of mechanical action, and indeed by mere contact with most kinds of materials. If one is not very careful indeed, either the sensitive red blood cells are crushed or burst open, a process known as haemolysis, or else the blood tends to clot and choke the blood vessels (thrombosis). Either way the prognosis is not good.

Nor are these by any means the only worries. An implanted organ must be expected to last for some years, ten or more preferably, if only because its implantation will entail a major surgical operation. This means that the materials from which it is made must survive conditions that are intensely fatiguing — a heart pulsates about 35 million times a year — and savagely corrosive, without the slightest prospect of routine maintenance.

Its power supply raises another formidable difficulty, for any man-made device with the capacity of the whole heart is going to supply up to seven watts of power — say one-hundredth of a horse-power — unceasingly, and hence must draw several times as much power to accommodate inevitable inefficiencies. What is more, the aim must obviously be to take up little or no more space than is occupied by the living heart.

Still more esoteric, for their solution depends upon a much deeper understanding of the physiology of the living heart and circulatory system, are such problems as how an artificial heart might be regulated. The heart 'booster' or temporary-assist devices we shall meet later do not have this problem, for they take their cue from the living organ. But a total heart replacement must be regulated by some other physiological factor. As one surgeon has put it, 'When a good-looking blonde walks down the street your heart speeds up. To make mechanical hearts respond to a blonde will not be easy.'

Another problem is to determine the best choice one can make for the wave form of the blood's pressure as it leaves the heart, for the condition that helped the heart to fail in the first place may benefit from a different waveform from the natural one.

Still more troublesome to duplicate is the role of the heart in monitoring the intricacies of the blood itself. These include the pH value (acidity), the amount of oxygen and carbon dioxide, the concentration of certain hormones, and of course blood pressure. Ideally, too, there should be some early warning of malfunction.

Clearly, then, the replacement of even so apparently simple an organ as the heart invokes problems far beyond the reach of the mechanical engineer. Probably no other single research pro-gramme today calls upon such a diversity of scientific disciplines, from mechanical and electronic engineering to psychological and sociological studies, and most of those that lie between.

In 1965 the National Heart Institute awarded half a dozen contracts to U.S. industry for feasibility studies into different aspects of the artificial heart, one of which went to the Convair division of General Dynamics Corporation in San Diego, the company that developed Atlas, America's first big space rocket. This company was invited to apply its skills in operational research, a relatively new approach to the management of large and complicated projects, to drawing up a programme for the development of a 'model T' artificial heart and the wherewithal for grafting it on to a quarter of a million people.

Dr W. A. Shafer of Convair, summarizing the conclusions of General Dynamics' studies, told an aerospace conference in Boston in November 1966 that beyond doubt the project was feasible, but that the cost until 1975 would amount to $1·8 billion — roughly $3,000 for each person who might expect to receive a new heart. His report pointed up eight key technical problems that would need to be solved. There were three bio-medical areas (coagulation and thrombosis; haemolysis, protein denaturation and blood trauma; and tissue rejection and foreign-body reaction), three technological areas (the power source; means of control and regulation; and materials), and two sociological areas, 'people problems' as he called them (legal, and economic).

In this chapter I am concerned primarily with the three technological areas, which apply to all work on artificial organs; although they can scarcely be discussed in isolation from the bio-medical areas. The 'people problems' are explored in more detail in the last chapter. But none of those eight areas can be treated in isolation, for they interact far too intimately with one another in a project of this complexity.

A HEART TAKES SHAPE

Let us turn now to some of the thirty-odd projects already under way around the world on the engineering of an artificial heart.

The essence of total replacement must be a double-action pump, a 'gentle' pump, one output from which forces freshly oxygenated blood from the lungs through the aorta to the entire body, while the other forces oxygen-depleted blood through the pulmonary artery to the lungs to replenish its oxygen (see Fig. 9).

Obviously, since the circulatory system is one continuous hydraulic circuit, the two outputs must be very carefully balanced in volume, otherwise pressure will build up somewhere and threaten to burst some of the blood vessels. Moreover, the pump must not allow a vacuum to form that could interrupt the flow of blood, perhaps also causing troubles akin to 'water hammer' in a domestic water system, that would be both disconcerting to the owner and damaging to his red blood cells.

The output of the compartment feeding the lungs (corresponding to the right ventricle) needs to be at a pressure of at least 20 millimetres of mercury, rising to 80 millimetres; that of the compartment feeding the rest of the body, 120 to 180 millimetres. Each must have a throughput of 1·5 to 8 litres of blood a minute, at a pumping rate of 60 to 160 cycles a minute.

This, then, is the basic specification for a total heart replacement. In actuality, most of the publicity that has surrounded attempts to provide patients with a man-made 'heart', including the operation on Mr Marcell DeRudder, a miner from Illinois, on April 21st, 1966, when Dr Michael E. DeBakey at the Methodist Hospital in Houston implanted a heart pump that kept the man alive for five days, has concerned only partial replacement of the heart. In other words, the idea has been to provide some kind of implantable auxiliary or 'booster' pump which, while taking its cue from the living organ, assumes some of the workload. A temporary-assist device of this sort could be valuable, for instance, where the heart itself is undernourished owing to fatty deposits in the coronary arteries, a condition known as atherosclerosis.

Some of the most ingenious engineering of gentle pumps has come from the Cleveland Clinic, where the surgeon Willem Kolff, who also invented an artificial kidney, heads research into the transplantation and implantation of organs. Writing of his early work on the artificial heart, Dr Kolff explains that his electrically driven hearts 'were a disappointment in several aspects. The electrical mechanisms were inefficient, too weak, too heavy and generated too much heat.'[1]

He talked over some of his problems with engineers at NASA's Lewis Research Center in Cleveland, who were accustomed to miniaturizing complex mechanisms. 'They responded with a startling suggestion: why not use compressed air instead of electricity as the power source? I recoiled; that idea would commit us to a system in which the power supply would have to be outside the body. I had visions of the possessor of an artificial heart walking around with something like a garden hose sticking out of his chest!'

All this happened in 1960. The pump that took shape in consequence comprises a simple sac of a plastic material (silicone rubber) within a rigid housing, also a silicone compound, having

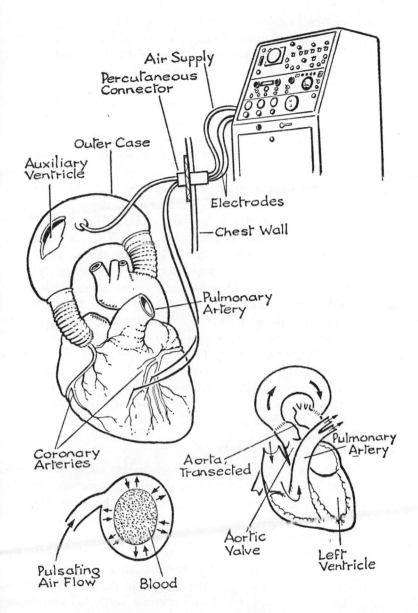

Air Supply

Percutaneous
Connector

Outer Case

Auxiliary
Ventricle

Electrodes

Chest Wall

Pulmonary
Artery

Coronary
Arteries

Aorta,
Transected

Pulmonary
Artery

Aortic
Valve

Left
Ventricle

Pulsating
Air Flow

Blood

Fig. 22. The Kantrowitz-Avco auxiliary ventricle, designed as a permanently
implantable heart-assist device

two one-way ball valves moulded in place. When compressed air is admitted to the housing through a fine plastic tube, it compresses the sac within, expelling its contents. Two such pumps could replace the basic function of the heart.

At the fifth attempt, Dr DeBakey's group in Houston successfully equipped a patient with a temporary-assist device for a period of ten days, in August 1966. Mrs Esperanza del Valle Vasquez, a Mexican housewife, was provided with a flexible sac of silicone rubber, driven by compressed air, that temporarily took over the work of her left ventricle — 60 per cent of the work of the heart. Then the rubber heart was removed and Mrs Vasquez went home, later to return to her work as a hairdresser.

A similar purpose motivates the work of Dr Adrian Kantrowitz in the Maimonides Hospital of Brooklyn, New York, who in 1964 reported that his auxiliary ventricle had functioned for up to forty-one hours in seventeen dogs, beginning immediately after closure of the chest. His approach, in the engineering of which he has been aided by a large aerospace company, the Avco Corporation, is to take the blood from the aorta at a propitious moment during the heart cycle, and return it to the aorta in a way that increases its energy yet lessens the work of the heart. To do this, a plastic sac is grafted into the aorta (see Plate 19). Rhythmic application of compressed air from a portable control unit outside the chest wall causes the sac to displace some fifteen millilitres of blood at each heart-beat (see Fig. 22).

TOTAL HEART REPLACEMENT

The comparatively simple devices discussed so far serve to illuminate some of the difficulties of total heart replacement, where one can no longer rely on the living heart for the more complex functions, yet the surgeon is severely restricted in the weight and volume of material he can deploy. One of these problems is a method of control. Kolff's two-pump heart replacement, for example, would still have the problem of finding some physiological factor that would relate the output to the body's requirements, which as we saw in Chapter 1 can surge between wide limits.

During the 1950s, a research team with the (then) Diamond Ordnance Fuze Laboratories of the U.S. Army in Washington,

D C., began to develop a new concept in control, where puffs and spurts of fluid (liquid or gas) could be used very similarly to bursts of electrons in electronic circuits. The new technique was called 'fluidics', and an early demonstration of its possibilities was an artificial heart pump for the support over long periods of failing hearts and blood circulations.

The important thing about fluidics is that it need use no moving parts. The circulatory system itself is of course a fluid system, so in principle at least the two are well matched. Kenneth E. Woodward of the now-renamed Harry Diamond Laboratories has since developed an implantable heart that is controlled by a 'fluid amplifier', a fluidic device in which the stream of compressed air driving the heart is switched back and forth between the two pumps automatically, by the pressure of blood in the pumps themselves. In one experiment by Dr Kolff, a calf was kept alive and in good shape for fifty hours by this system.

Fluidic controls look very promising for many control functions connected with implanted mechanisms, for they can be made extremely small and from materials the body will accept. Moreover, they are extremely robust and unaffected by vibration or by seepage of traces of body fluids, unlike electronic circuits. Above all, they are highly compatible with the several fluid systems of which the body itself is composed (see also Fig. 26).

But while fluidics can control the artificial heart itself, some way is still needed of matching this control to the body's demands.

Quite another fluid approach has been adopted at the Hospital of the University of Pennsylvania in Philadelphia, where a team led by an engineer, Adair Rogers, recognizing the problem of the total heart replacement to be largely hydrodynamic in nature, is developing a closed system that works hydraulically, is controlled hydraulically, and simulates as far as possible the natural organ.

Rogers's artificial heart transmits hydraulic energy across a plastic membrane separating the working fluid from the blood itself (see Fig. 23). In this way the contents of the ventricles are squeezed into their respective arteries without the blood ever coming into contact with the pump itself.

The heart is driven by a small turbo-pump used to store up energy by expanding a bellows, that can be released as fluid pressure to compress the blood-filled ventricles. The idea at

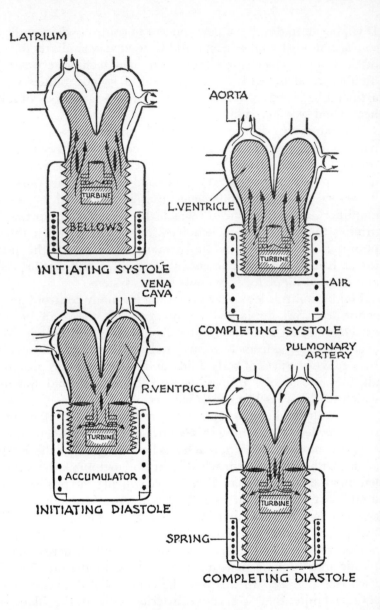

FIG. 23. Four steps in the cycle of an electro-hydraulic artificial heart, under development at the University of Pennsylvania, eventually for total implantation

present is that the electrically driven pump shall draw its power from outside the body, through a tube that passes through the skin, and through a silicone 'plaster' he has designed, that anchors the emerging leads and provides a barrier against infection.

The systolic and diastolic phases of Rogers's heart are reproduced by a three-way hydraulic valve, comprising two circular plates; the lower one remaining stationary while the other slides. These plates are so slotted that fluid is forced either upwards into the ventricles, simulating systole, or downwards from the ventricles, simulating diastole. The entire cycle will be timed by the inflation and deflation of the spring-loaded bellows, collapsed by atmospheric pressure (which means of course that the heart will respond to changes in altitude and weather).

This terse description neglects to mention the many ingenious refinements Rogers is designing into the hydraulic heart, such as the magnetic system that deftly switches the heart from its diastolic to its systolic phase; the means that ensure a lower pressure in the right ventricle (supplying the lungs) than the left; and the way it controls its own output, over a range of 30 to 100 per cent of its capacity, according to changes in pressure of the return flow from the veins.

The upper portion of Rogers's heart, corresponding to the heart itself, is intended to be implanted within the chest, and will eventually be no larger than the heart it replaces. The lower portion, the power and control unit, will be implanted directly below, in the abdomen, where it will occupy about twice the volume of the living heart, roughly twelve centimetres long by ten centimetres in diameter. A tube through the wall of the abdomen will supply power and atmospheric pressure (see Plate 20).

The intention is that the entire mechanism shall be tested, adjusted, encapsulated and sterilized ready for the surgeon to graft into place.

IMPLANTABLE POWERPACKS

If the engineer is ever to provide surgeons with a truly implantable mechanism, such as an artificial heart or kidney, or even with electronic stimulators, he must find some new source of power. Present pacemakers derive their energy from small batteries, of strictly limited life. But any scheme that requires periodic replacement, necessitating surgery, must be treated as inherently unsatisfactory. Other inconveniences apart, an ephemeral source of power would be a constant reminder to the owner of his ultimate dependency upon a machine.

One alternative to the battery is a radioisotope. This is an unstable variety of an element which spontaneously disintegrates, giving out radiation in the process. Radiation from this source is already well-established in medicine in a host of diagnostic and therapeutic roles.

One of the most ambitious projects in the quest for biological power aims to implant a fragment of radioactive material, the emanations from which would be converted into electricity by heating a small thermocouple to about 150 °C. Early in 1966 the U.S. Atomic Energy Commission embarked upon what its chairman, Dr Glenn T. Seaborg, once told me would be the most satisfying project he could bring to fruition during his tenure of office: an atom-powered heart pacemaker with a life of ten years or more, several times as long as the best batteries can promise.

With wry irony, the device will be powered by an isotope of plutonium, the metal which devastated Nagasaki. But 'Fat Man', as the bomb was called, was made of plutonium-239, whereas the lighter isotope plutonium-238 disintegrates more leisurely, releasing only relatively feeble alpha particles. The A.E.C.'s specification calls for an implantable cardiac pacemaker, no dimension of which exceeds six centimetres, built into which is the radioactive plutonium, so shielded that the wearer will be put at risk neither by the radiation — plutonium is reckoned the most poisonous of metals — nor the heat developed (see Fig. 17).

In fact, since the wearer is likely to be middle-aged or elderly, it may be acceptable to take a slightly more tolerant attitude to radiation, in view of the pacemaker's role as a life preserver. Nevertheless, an extremely pure form of plutonium-238 will be needed, to avoid the deadly gamma radiation that impurities may emanate. This applies also should other radioisotopes of long life but feeble radiation, such as the beta-emitting isotopes of thulium and promethium, or tritium, be tried. The cost of their purification is likely to bulk large in the final cost of this kind of pacemaker.

Some measure of the complexity of the task may be gauged from the estimated cost of the *initial* phase of the A.E.C.'s programme, which was $500,000–$750,000 to bring experimental models to the stage of short-term testing. The Atomic Energy Authority in Britain is developing a pacemaker with an output of 540 micro-watts. Both countries have plans for animal tests during 1969.

The present objective is a powerpack with an output of 30 to 100 microwatts (millionths of a watt), but it is the hope of its sponsors, the National Heart Institute and Newark Beth Israel Hospital, that much more powerful isotopic generators will prove possible. It has been worked out that the power source for an artificial heart must deliver 1·5 to 4 watts of continuous power, and up to 7 watts to cope with vigorous exercise. The best power sources we can envisage at present have conversion efficiencies no greater than 15 per cent, leaving anything up to 25 watts of heat for the body's own temperature control system to absorb and eliminate. But, leaving aside the heat-exchange aspect, where might we find an unflagging source of power of about 30 watts to serve an artificial heart?

In the spring of 1967 the A.E.C. announced design studies it was sponsoring into the possibility of an isotope-fired engine, with a heat-exchanger cooled by the bloodstream and a control system regulating its output between 1 and 7 watts. The idea was to arrive at a design that could be implanted somewhere in the abdomen. Not the least of the problems will be to anchor such an engine securely, for very small pressures on bone can cause its distortion.

Incredible as it may sound, four kinds of heat engine, two driven by steam and two by helium gas, are now being studied as prospects for implantation. Typical is the closed-cycle steam engine in which water would be boiled by the emanations of a highly purified radioisotope such as plutonium-238 or thulium-171. Exhaust steam from the engine would pass to a condenser, serving as a heat-sink, the condensate from which would be pumped back to the boiler. The idea at present is to couple the piston directly to a hydraulic pump, that in turn would drive the blood pump. Aerojet-General is developing a free-piston engine using the Stirling cycle, designed to draw 35 watts from a radioisotope source, and deliver 7 watts for pumping.

I

Another possible source is a battery which, instead of requiring periodic replacement, is continuously replenished—by the body itself. Such a battery is usually called a fuel cell. This is a system in which some convenient fuel is 'burnt' at the surface of an electrode by a process that sets up a flow of electrons—an electric current. Fuel cells are being developed most energetically just now, as a compact and remarkably efficient source of power for such purposes as an electric car and for spacecraft.

Up to a point the idea of using the body's tissues as the electrolyte for a built-in fuel cell is a most elegant one, for they offer an electrically conductive moistness that is kept warm and continuously replenished—the perfect electrolyte. Moreover, the efficiency of a fuel cell is potentially much higher than other energy conversion schemes. Electrodes of two different metals, buried close to but not touching each other, could provide such a cell. Two Canadian scientists, O. Z. Roy and R. W. Wehnert, of the National Research Council in Ottawa, have drawn enough power in this way to drive a heart pacemaker (see Plate 21).[2] There is enough oxygen in the tissues, they have found, to raise 300 microwatts.

The first big snag is precisely the one that impedes the fuel cell's progress elsewhere, namely savage corrosion of the electrodes; although the Canadians believe their powerpack is good for 10 years. Another is that in order to generate more power it would probably be necessary to construct the fuel cell in the large colon, where the considerable bacteriological activity might be harnessed. Quite long leads would then be needed to bring the power to the point of use, increasing the risk of a breakage through fatigue brought about by the constant movement of the body.

There is yet another difficulty, more fundamental, in as much as the flow of electricity appears to damage cells at the point where electrodes are stitched to the heart. As a result the circuits' resistance rises beyond the pacemaker's capacity, and the heart simply switches off.

J. J. Konikoff, a General Electric systems engineer who has been exploring some of the possibilities for implantable powerpacks, recently summed up the living fuel cells as 'theoretically interesting, but still in the stage where problems are concerned with physiological acceptance. Thus, unless an alternate method is conceived it appears that the application is impractical.'

But if a free source of power within the body raises problems too formidable for present technology, why not introduce the current from outside? Technically it should be possible to pass leads through the skin, as is done with cannulae for the artificial kidney.

Unfortunately for the engineer, the skin more than any other tissue is continually breaking down and being replaced, and a permanent seal that is impervious to infective organisms is not easy to secure. Leads penetrating the wall of the chest could be particularly dangerous, owing to the high mortality rate of chest infections. Cannulae, on the other hand, can always be shifted to another limb to allow an infected site to heal.

But there are less clumsy ways of introducing electric power, for example at microwave frequencies, a technique already being explored by electrical engineers as a future prospect for transmitting power over long distances without need for cables or overhead power lines. One American worker claims to have transmitted as much as fifty watts through the skin for long periods without apparently damaging the tissues, though others are wary of the risks of microwave radiation. It may also mean the wearer must carry a transmitter, probably correctly placed to secure the most efficient transfer of energy, and so would be constantly reminded of his affliction.

One possible way of avoiding the need constantly to carry a transmitter is being explored by the McDonnell Douglas aerospace company, under a contract awarded by the National Heart Institute. It is to use microwave radiation intermittently — at night for instance — to reactivate a chemical compound implanted in a small engine inside the body. The activated chemical would then liberate heat that could be used to expand a gas. Pneumatic power generated in this way would be piped through fine plastic pipes to rhythmically compress the sacs of an artificial heart. The company hopes to keep the engine down to the size of a grapefruit and limit its moving parts to a single oscillating member, used to raise and lower the pressure of gas to the prosthesis.

In Britain a physicist, Dr L. Juhasz, has pursued the related idea of burying a solar cell just beneath the skin. This is a device that converts light waves straight into electricity. The light waves can come from exposure to sunlight, by implanting the solar cell at the side of the neck for instance, or artificially by occasionally exposing the cell to a lamp. The output of the solar cell would then be used to keep fully charged a small rechargeable battery, implanted in the body, ensuring a uniform output of electricity. But the amount of power made available in this way seems likely to be very small.

On present showing, the best long-term prospect is to harness the body's own energy, for even when resting our bodies dissipate about fifty watts to the air around us. Some of this energy might be harnessed by mechanical means, and the mechanical motion converted into a flow of electricity.

Perhaps the most obvious way would be a 'haemo-electric' scheme which harnessed the flow of blood to turn a turbogenerator. One obstacle is the relatively slow speed of blood, a maximum of a metre a second at the point where it leaves the heart, which means inconveniently large coils on the generator. Another is the fragility of the red blood cells, which could be destroyed by the turbine faster than the body can replace them.

There are certain crystals which, when squeezed, generate a small amount of electricity. The most familiar example is the 'needle' of a phonograph pick-up. The effect was discovered by two French brothers in the 1880s, who called it piezoelectrique, from the Greek word *piezein*, to press. Now within the living body are a number of structures that rhythmically exert pressure, unremittingly, throughout its life: the heart, for example, as it pulsates, and the chest as it rises and falls. So the possibility exists that by burying a piezoelectric crystal in some suitable cranny it could be caused to emit an unceasing flow of electrical energy.

The idea appeals to the engineer because it is simple and there is very little to go wrong. It is attractive to the physiologist for quite another reason. There is evidence that piezoelectricity is a fundamental property of living biological tissues anyway, for its occurrence has been demonstrated in wood and silk fibres, and in bone, tendon and hair. In fact, this electrical response to mechanical forces may somehow cause the growth of bone and other tissue to adapt to outside influences, such as pressure.

A scientist, George H. Myers, and a surgeon, Victor Parsonnet,

132

of New York, have constructed a piezoelectric 'clothespeg' (see Plate 22). The motion of the aorta is transmitted to piezoelectric crystals by means of bellows. When pegged around the aorta of a dog, the arms of this device were flexed by the surges of blood, generating about 4 millionths of a watt per second per heart-beat. The inventors expect about four times this output from a human heart-beat.

Instead of simply accepting a train of electrical impulses at the rate the energizing tissue happens to be moving, Myers and Parsonnet explored the possibility of storing this energy mechanically, for release at the rate they required. A watch movement is just a mechanism, built to very high standards of reliability. They collaborated with Egbert Van Haaften of the Bulova Watch Company to develop a self-winding mechanism that is kept fully wound by the motion of the diaphragm or heart, acting through a lever. This arm winds a spring, which in turn drives a cam that is arranged to strike a piezoelectric crystal. The movement can thus be set to generate electric pulses at the rate required.

Whether devices of this kind can be scaled up in output to yield the watts wanted by an artificial organ is still uncertain. The muscle harnessed to the purpose may grow tired of exerting itself against the large and relatively unyielding area of crystal. On the other hand, piezoelectricity also works in reverse—the crystal will bend in response to a voltage. This principle has been tried at the University of Pennsylvania to construct an artificial heart, the membranes of which are very thin sheets of crystal which flex in response to a pacemaker.

At this stage, certainly, the simplicity and reliability of the piezoelectric approach seems to guarantee it a place in surgical engineering.

WHAT SHALL WE MAKE IT FROM?

This question rarely poses more problems for the engineer than when he is dealing with the living body, the tissues of which bear scant relationship to any man-made material. Even the load-bearing members, the bones, have a complexity of performance that far surpasses present concepts of engineering design.

Much of the human body consists of many different kinds of proteins. Single-cell proteins have already been synthesized, such as those now made from oil by microbiological action, in Scotland and elsewhere, which when suitably flavoured afford an edible food bearing some similarity to meat. But the gulf between this considerable achievement of the chemists and the idea of manufacturing proteins from which surgical structures might be fashioned — polypeptides, perhaps — remains a large one. And far beyond that lies the dream of synthesizing a living tissue.

To return to earth, however, the engineer who would simply substitute for nature's tissues already appears to have an inexhaustible spectrum of materials from which to choose : from the softest fabrics or foams to the strongest or hardest of metals. Unfortunately an existence, even briefly, in living tissues imposes cruel stresses against which very few materials are proof, while foreign materials in turn can gravely perturb the living environment.[3]

The most obvious trouble that can arise is an infection, by introducing micro-organisms. This may be easy to counter in the case of metals, which are readily sterilized, but more troublesome should the material be at all sensitive to heat. Again, the warm, corrosive body fluids, rather like seawater in composition, may leach substances from the material — substances used, say, in the preparation of a particular plastic — that are themselves toxic and which ravage the adjoining tissues. A third problem arises should the live tissues prove allergic to the material, a situation which can arise when contact is merely through the skin.

A fourth and most serious source of conflict between living tissues and their imitation is called the foreign-body reaction, where the unnatural material is deemed by the body's defence mechanisms to be an undesirable intruder. This provokes a response from the surrounding tissues that will vary in its intensity from a normal 'repair response' through an 'inflammatory response' to varying degrees of 'immunological response'. At one end of this spectrum of foreign-body reaction is the response provoked by inert substances, where the processes of repair merely attempt to encapsulate and wall off the intruding substance or, if it is so constructed, to mingle with it. At the other end is the response provoked by living material from another source — 'not-self' tissue as it is called — culminating in total mismatch and an acute rejection crisis. The immunological response is discussed in more detail in the next chapter.

134

The tissues of the body divide, broadly speaking, into two kinds: soft tissues (such as the connective tissues, muscles and blood vessels) and hard tissues (principally bones, and also cartilage). The two kinds present quite different problems, but eight essential criteria for accepting a substitute for living tissue, defined by a British scientist, Dr John T. Scales, in 1953, still hold good today.

Scales suggested that the substitute (1) should not be affected physically by soft tissues of the body, (2) should be chemically inert, (3) should provoke no inflammation or foreign-body reaction, (4) should not promote cancer, (5) should induce no state of allergy or hypersensitivity, (6) should resist mechanical strains, (7) should be workable to the desired shape, and (8) should be sterilizable.[4]

This disarmingly simple set of criteria is actually a formidable barrier to the progress of internal prostheses, for although a very small number of materials closely approach these standards they do not afford the range of properties that will probably be needed for a complete mechanism. To take a familiar example, no man-made substitute that would be physiologically acceptable comes anywhere near bone in strength for a given weight (three times as strong as timber, and half the strength of mild steel yet only a third of its weight) and in its capacity to absorb the shock of a sudden load. This is because bone is a structure, rather than a homogeneous material, and develops its properties in response to the loads imposed upon it.

The soft tissues of the body span an enormous range of 'softness', from the fluidity of blood at one end to the comparative firmness of a piece of muscle—a heart valve or a large blood vessel, for instance. In fact, the entire body with the exception of the skeleton, teeth and nails is composed of soft tissue. These tissues are constantly irrigated by body fluids. The cells of which they are composed die and are continually replaced. The entire mass is kept unremittingly in motion in a normally active person.

The engineer shies from conditions as savage as these. His customary approach is to try to insulate his materials from the worst excesses of the working environment; but this is not often possible in biomedical engineering. Instead, the problems of fatigue—the weariness that can end in catastrophic failure—in materials kept constantly in motion, and of 'stress corrosion' in materials exposed simultaneously to chemical and mechanical forces, must be countered with a special breed of materials, cultivated for the purpose.

There is a further obstacle to the body's acceptance of substitutes, which is the effect they may have on that most ubiquitous of body fluids, blood. Fortunately enough, blood shows great readiness to clot when in contact with anything but its natural environment, thereby rapidly sealing all but the most serious leaks from the circulatory system. Contact with most foreign materials also promotes some measure of clotting—and it needs very little clotted blood to choke a vital artery or obstruct a heart valve. Compatibility with blood remains one of the most troublesome factors in finding substitutes for tissues.

Nevertheless, most of the soft tissues of the body have successfully been substituted, albeit through the use of a surprisingly small number of materials. Of these, one of the most valuable has proved to be a family of polymers known as the silicones.

When carefully prepared, in very pure form, silicone compounds appear to be adequately inert for many internal applications (see Plates 23 and 24). At the same time, they can be formulated to a spectrum of properties that reaches from the fluidity of breast tissue to the rigidity of a jawbone. There is fine irony in the fact that these and other materials which have proved reasonably satisfactory for one of the most exacting roles the technologist can devise all come under the heading of 'plastics'—materials once regarded as cheap substitutes for the real thing.

The silicones, which according to their hardness and other characteristics are variously known as silicone fluids, silicone rubbers or silicone resins, are essentially compounds of silicon and oxygen. This is a rather special branch of organic chemistry where silicon replaces carbon as the vital ingredient. First synthesized around the turn of the century, the polysiloxane (silicone) structure, with its backbone of silicon atoms, has proved to be one of the most unreactive of polymeric structures. For many purposes the prevailing weakness of these compounds is the way they are totally ignored by living tissues, for ideally the surgeon often would welcome some promotion of fibroblastic activity—the forming of scar tissue, which should help to anchor an implant securely in place. In its absence the implant must be buried as deeply and firmly as possible, to prevent its displacement, and the possible erosion of the live tissues surrounding it.

The list of soft tissues, other than organs, augmented or replaced by a silicone implant is almost complete today. One important area of reconstruction is cosmetic surgery, primarily concerned with the head and face, where the plastic surgeon can now repair features ravaged by accident or disease, or congenitally inadequate. Rigid 'armatures' that reconstruct ears, columellae and struts that remodel noses, sponge for reshaping cheeks and chins, fluids that replace the vitreous fluid of the eye to repair otherwise hopelessly detached retinas, are all familiar to the plastic surgeon today.

Even mammary tissue has been imitated, by T. D. Cronin who, in 1963, announced his 'natural feel prosthesis', a silicone rubber sac that comes in several sizes, filled with a silicone jelly which is stiff enough not to leak should the artificial breast become damaged in an accident. The sac has a backing of Dacron mesh and is implanted beneath the natural breast, stitched to and suspended from the chest wall itself. Fibroblastic activity then helps to support the artificial breast.

Very often alloplasty—the reconstructive process—is purely cosmetic, but its value to the patient can nonetheless be profound. Psychologically the patient may benefit enormously, as is evidenced by some of the 'before and after' photographs in medical literature. The girl whose chin, once receding, is now firm and shapely may well see her future quite differently, so that her entire personality responds to the new contours.

In 1966 a Vancouver prison hospital reported that prisoners whose facial disfigurements are corrected are less likely to return to crime. More recently Masters and Greaves have introduced the term Quasimodo complex, defined as 'anxiety, hostility, social withdrawal, and abnormal personality traits produced by emotional reactions to physical deformity'.[5] As New Scientist remarked, 'Ugly as sin apparently contains an ultimate truth, and handsome does as handsome is.'

Probably the most extensive use of implanted silicones is a duct known as the ventriculo-caval shunt, used to rectify a condition known as hydrocephalus or 'water-on-the-brain', sometimes found in newborn babies. Such a child was born, in 1955, to John Holter, an American toolmaker who in a race with death devised a duct that would drain off the excess cerebrospinal fluid from the brain cavity and absorb it in the bloodstream. This shunt, made from silicone rubber, has two tiny valves of the same material that open when the pressure builds up. It leads from the brain through the skull (although still beneath the skin) and into the throat, where it enters the jugular vein. Thus it remains permanently in contact with several kinds of tissue—brain tissue, bone, muscle, skin and venous blood: a most severe test of compatibility.

For the moment the silicone compounds afford the most versatile range of physical properties in any material that is compatible with living tissues. But other materials, no less compatible, have found more specific purpose. For example, a replacement for the mitral valve of the heart, developed in a London hospital, is made entirely of polypropylene.

The mitral valve, linking atrium and ventricle on the left side of the organ, thus known for its resemblance to a bishop's mitre, when seriously diseased will leak blood, so that the heart's performance is constantly below par. It has been emphasized before that blood is a very sensitive fluid, highly intolerant of the sudden decompression that occurs when, for example, a mechanical valve closes abruptly. For several years now the most successful means of repair has been a ball valve developed by two Americans, Dr Albert Starr, professor of surgery in the University of Oregon Medical School, and a retired engineer, Mr M. Lowell Edwards, and first implanted in September 1960. The Starr-Edwards valve comprises a silicone resin ball poppet that bobs inside a stainless steel cage in response to blood pressure (see Plates 25 and 27).

This valve showed convincingly that a mechanical valve could do the job. Somewhat similar valves, by the same inventors, can replace the high-pressure aortic and also the tricuspid valves, and indeed have replaced all three in the same patient.[6] By the beginning of 1967 about 36,000 ball valves of this kind had been implanted. About one ball poppet in a thousand, however, becomes distorted or damaged in service, for reasons still not understood—although of the first 30,000 valves of this kind implanted the 29 failures were all in aortic valves.[7]

Professor Hugh Benthall and his colleagues in the department of experimental surgery at Hammersmith Hospital in London have since developed a new kind of mitral valve, quite different in construction, made wholly of plastic. Little more than two inches across, it has two simple plastic mouldings – a seat, and a flap valve than can move very freely, restrained only from leaving the seat entirely and from rotating (which could cause turbulence in the bloodstream). The seat has a 'tyre' of woven polypropylene mesh, which the surgeon secures by two dozen sutures to the wall of the heart. Three months after the operation the valve is truly implanted, with living tissue mingling with the mesh to hold it securely in place. South African surgeons have also designed heart valves of polypropylene (see Plate 26). Even so, polypropylene is still not the perfect material – it abrads too easily, and can also cause clots.

Diseases of the heart and blood vessels may affect nearly 20 per cent of the population of the U.S.A., the National Institutes of Health believe, 'and may cost the Nation up to 25 billion dollars annually in medical care, lost productivity and wages, and future earnings by those succumbing to these diseases', according to a recent report.[8]

Since the start of this century surgeons have sought materials that might replace faulty plumbing in the arterial system of the body. (The veins incidentally are far less susceptible to disease.) The first attempts to graft blood vessels were made with cadaver vessels which, although dead tissue, served simply as a 'skeleton' on which new tissue would form. But they were hard to obtain and preserve, and sometimes introduced faults of their own. Dr Alexis Carrel (1873–1944) and others used a variety of substances – metals, plastics and glass among them – but none worked well until the advent of woven synthetic fabrics, and especially of Terylene (polyester).

Today, prosthetic blood vessels down to a quarter of an inch in diameter are knitted from Terylene filament yarn by a technique first developed at the Philadelphia Textile Institute.[9] Bifurcated (forked) and multi-branch tubes can all be made in this way, as Plate 27 shows. The fabric is treated chemically to reduce its porosity and minimize the loss of blood until fresh tissue has mingled with and sealed up the new graft. Another important development was the work of Dr Michael DeBakey who introduced

139

a permanent 'crimp' into these vessels to prevent their collapse when bent.

Vessels made in this way have been used successfully to repair or replace natural vessels from the aorta itself to those feeding the brain, so often the source of cerebral damage. They retain their strength in body tissues for years, yet can be cut and shaped by the surgeon with scissors or scalpel. Some miles of plastic blood vessels have already been implanted by surgeons.

The elusive blend of properties required of a material that is to be buried in the body is beginning to attract the attention of polymer chemists, who see possibilities in grafting appropriate chemical structures on to polymeric 'backbones' already proven to be adequately unreactive, in order to make them more compatible for a given role.

Clotting remains a serious difficulty in replacing parts of the circulatory system, the heart especially. A chemical called heparin is very useful in delaying clotting. It is already present in the body—in fact, as a surgeon once put it to me, we would go solid without it. In replacing a diseased heart valve or blood vessel with one of plastic the surgeon will first swab the spare part with this chemical.

Ideally, of course, this anticlotting factor should be 'built into' the spare part. This may become possible through grafting, and a technique has been developed at the Battelle Memorial Institute, whereby chemically active sites are created in the plastic. Heparin then attaches itself to these sites to give a surface possessed of the desired anticoagulating properties—clot-proof, that is. Many different kinds of plastic can be 'heparinized' in this way, including the membranes used in artificial kidneys. Unfortunately there is now strong evidence that the anticoagulant effect of heparin gradually wears out. More permanent anticoagulants are urgently needed.

It may eventually be possible by similar 'proofing' processes to increase a material's resistance to degradation by a particular enzyme, or its propensity for stimulating the growth of scar tissue, that will help to secure it in place.

THE LARGEST ORGAN

Imitating his skin affords man's technology and imagination a special challenge, since the skin is the largest organ of the body—

and of course the most vulnerable. This sheath, about two square metres in area, has a multitude of functions: among them to keep body fluids in and foreign substances out, and to regulate the body's temperature and blood pressure (many limbless thalidomide babies died from overheating, because their skin area was too small). It is the body's first line of defence, yet at the same time provides both a sense of touch and an aspect of sexual attraction. Love itself has been described as the contact of epidermises. 'Skin deep' — actually a matter of anything up to four millimetres — is an expression that scarcely warrants the disparaging overtones usually implied.

Unlike most other organs the skin has tremendous powers of restoration, which is one reason for the success of skin grafting in plastic surgery. But the graft must come from the same person, for so far skin has proved immunologically more resistant to transplanting than internal organs.

The cells of the skin are regenerated much faster than those of the soft tissues generally; but not, unfortunately, quickly enough should very large areas become damaged, as may be the case with a severe burn. Roughly speaking, the prognosis is bad if more than a quarter of the total body surface has been badly burnt, for a denuded body will lose fluid at an alarming rate and the risk of serious infection becomes considerable. (The surgeon has a technique known as the 'rule of nines' for quickly assessing the burnt area, which reckons each leg, thigh and arm and the head as 9 per cent of the total area, and the front and back of the torso as 18 per cent apiece.)

A famous American surgeon, Joseph E. Murray, told a C.I.B.A. Symposium in London that 'Ideally, an entirely new suit of skin ought to be available to put on the patient after the burnt skin has been removed. It is a rather eerie experience', he continued, 'for the surgeon to see a severely burnt patient, one who has 50 to 60 per cent of his total body surface damaged, let us say, walk into the hospital or into the first-aid station feeling quite comfortable [a consequence, presumably, of shock] and asking for a cigarette. The surgeon knows that the individual within a matter of hours will be dead. Possibly, if that new suit of skin were available for use, immediate excision and resurfacing of the whole burnt area would be life-saving.'[10]

Unfortunately, artificial skins are usually quickly floated off the bare surface by the exuding fluid. The nearest we have come to that new suit of skin is the idea of immersing burned patients in a bath of a liquid silicone compound. F. J. Gerow and his colleagues reported such a practice at the Third International Congress of Plastic Surgery in Washington in 1963. They claimed it left their patients almost free from pain, that there was less infection, and that patients were ready for grafting sooner. The great difficulty, of course, is to keep the bath sterile for any length of time.

One might visualize Murray's new suit of skin starting with the patient being dipped in a fluid that cold-sets to form a flexible and 'breathable' film, after which he would be nursed on an air-cushion bed that kept him floating gently out of contact with his surroundings.

It is precisely because a healthy skin provides such a strong barrier against infection, and moreover wears out and is restored at a high rate, that the problem of percutaneous connections — those that pass through the skin — appears so troublesome. Scribner and others have achieved fair measure of success with their fluid coupling for the artificial kidney, but the difficulties of coupling power — electric, hydraulic or pneumatic — into the body, and especially into the chest, appear much greater.

Many kinds of percutaneous leads and access plugs have been proposed that appear perfectly satisfactory for short-term use. Such a plug, of silicone resin for use with a booster heart, is sketched in Fig. 22. But a simple and germproof seal for long-term use, which will certainly be needed at any rate until the technology of miniature power sources has caught up with progress in artificial organs, still eludes the bio-engineer.

There is a rather special kind of implant with a history that goes back to the sixth century B.C., when the Indian surgeon Susruta was in practice. This is the suture, or stitch, used to reunite severed tissues. The various natural fibres used by Susruta have since been supplanted by silk and gut, and more recently by man-made fibres like Terylene; stainless steel staples have also been used successfully, especially by Russian and East German surgeons, in rejoining the smaller blood vessels, and closing the stomach or gut. Nevertheless, suturing is a relatively crude procedure when compared with adhesive bonding – 'gluing' – and rapid developments in the performance of adhesives have steadily encouraged the surgeon, since 1955 particularly, to seek an adhesive for living tissues.

The conditions are formidable indeed, for in addition to meeting Scales's criteria (p. 135) the adhesive must be a cold-setting one, that will hold the moist, fat-containing tissues together for a week or ten days, until normal healing has taken over. Ideally, too, the bond should be flexible.

A dozen years of investigation has brought us near these requirements. Research chemists with the Battelle Memorial Institute, for example, have come up with a formula that seems much more successful than early adhesives. Their starting point was gelatine, a naturally occurring protein that chemically resembles connective tissue. Gelatine is itself adhesive in character but is weakened by moisture. In combination with formaldehyde and resorcinol, however, it provides an adhesive that has performed satisfactorily both *in vitro* and *in vivo*.

Battelle's blend of gelatine, resorcinol and formaldehyde (G.R.F.) is by no means the last word in surgical adhesives, but gives cause for optimism about a technique likely to prove of inestimable value in the repair of unhealthy or ageing tissues. Probably no single formula will fulfil every surgical need, but a family of adhesives may evolve that includes, say, a specially quick-setting version for certain repairs, or a particularly strong or ductile adhesive for the repair of highly elastic tissue. In fact, the Battelle team announced a further advance in 1967, with an adhesive based on diiso-cyanate, which showed initial bond strengths greater than that of the muscle tissue to which it had been applied.

Quite another matter are the problems of replacing, or even strengthening, the supporting tissues of the body, the bones. There are a total of 206 of them, and they mate and interact in a most intricate manner to support and protect the softer tissues.

Metals are the obvious materials for this purpose, although mostly they match neither the strength of bone for a given weight nor its unique ability to absorb and counteract the effect of a sudden load. Nor, as many surgeons – and many more patients – have discovered to their cost, will most metals survive lengthy immersion in the brines that irrigate our tissues. Nevertheless, roughly a million orthopaedic screws alone are implanted in Americans every year.

A lot of the pioneering work in orthopaedic surgery was carried out, by Sir Arbuthnot Lane in Britain and W. D. Sherman in the U.S.A., early this century—before stainless steels were even discovered (1913). Both these surgeons, and many others since, used ordinary steel plates and screws to make their repairs, and the hideous consequences can be seen in a number of collections that more enlightened surgeons have made of bits of metal they subsequently removed from the hapless patients. Only too plainly in many cases have both the choice of material and the physical form of the repair itself defied all known rules of engineering.

Commenting on this, Dr John Scales, whom we met earlier in this chapter, has written: 'Surgery, while becoming a science, is still an art and those who practise it are jealous of the freedom enjoyed by artists. They resent and oppose any suggestion or attempt to impose restriction on their freedom of choice of material or method of treatment.'[11] It is a comment, by an internationally recognized authority, worth recalling in the light of current enthusiasm among cardiac surgeons for heart transplants.

Let us look first at the question of corrosion, a curiously complex process of deterioration that is influenced not merely by chemical considerations, although these are pretty savage in living tissues, but also by physical stresses and strains upon the material. So we find, for example, that metal surfaces rubbing together under inadequate lubrication may deteriorate rapidly through 'fretting' corrosion. Again corrosion is deeply influenced by contact between different metals, which when moistened may form an electrochemical couple or battery, in which one metal will be eaten away. This can arise when, say, a bronze screw is used to secure a steel plate to a bone, and even when flakes of metal from the surgeon's mallet are left adhering to the head of an orthopaedic pin.

Only recently have research workers versed in the complexities of corrosion turned to the living environment. The results confirm how small is the list of truly satisfactory metals available to the orthopaedic surgeon. Many expensive alloys normally chosen for their resistance to corrosion have been found wanting. Hoar and

Plate 26. Heart simulator used to test the function of mitral heart valve, of polypropylene, developed by the South African Council for Scientific and Industrial Research in Pretoria

Plate 27. Plastic 'spare parts'. Left to right, Starr-Edwards mitral valve, aortic valve leaflet and (*held by surgeon*) aortic valve; also crimped and bifurcated blood vessels

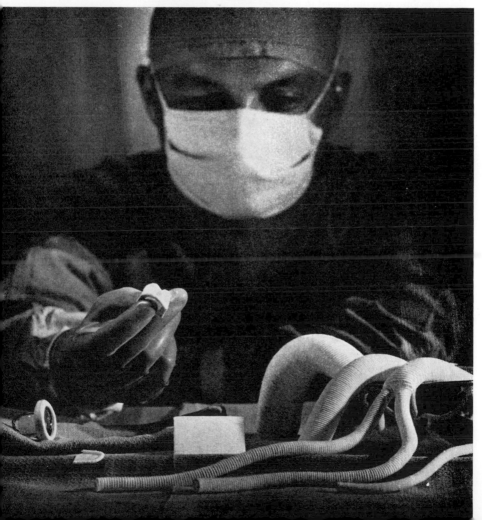

Plate 28. These two cobalt-alloy bearing specimens were tested under exactly the same conditions in a hip-joint simulator at Lewis Research Center. The one on the left has a hexagonal crystal structure; that on the right a cubic structure

Plate 29. Knee joint of cobalt-chromium alloy designed by the Institute of Orthopaedics in London. The joint was implanted in a girl of twenty in 1954

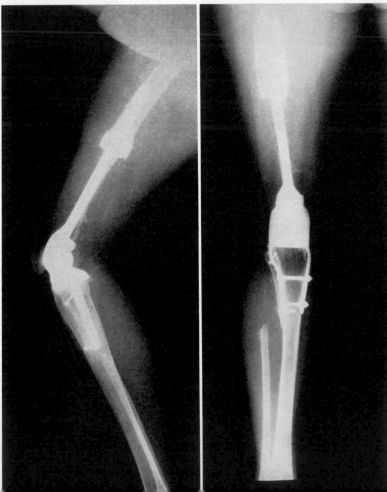

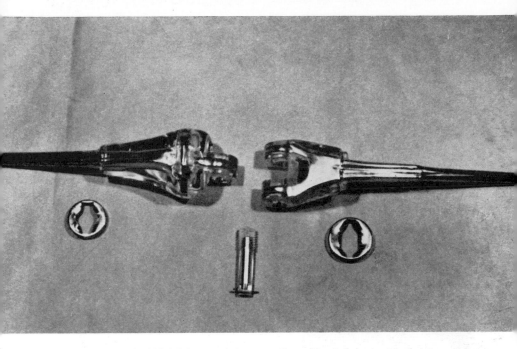

Plate 30. Japanese design of artificial knee, of clear acrylic resin reinforced with stainless steel

Plate 31. Implanting an artificial knee joint in a Tokyo operating theatre

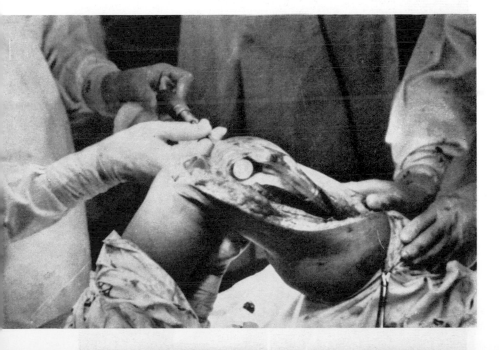

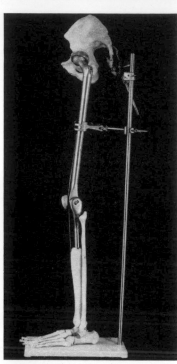

Plate 32. Cobalt-chromium alloy and titanium implant displayed at the Combined Meeting of the Scandinavian and British Orthopaedic Associations in September 1967. It is believed to be the largest implantable prosthesis ever assembled

Plate 33. (below) Surgeon fashions a piece of denatured bone before implantation

Plate 34. (facing page 144) Mr Louis Washkansky, the world's first recipient of a human heart, 12 days after the transplant operation. Mr Washkanksy died a week later

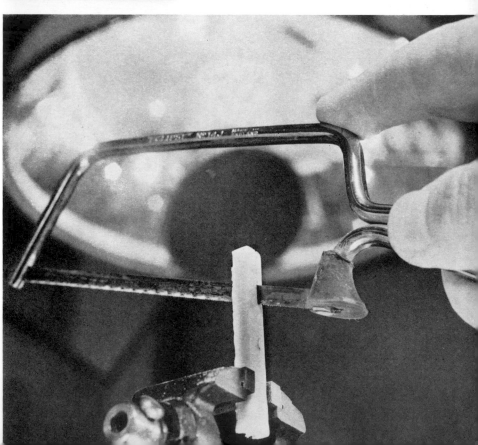

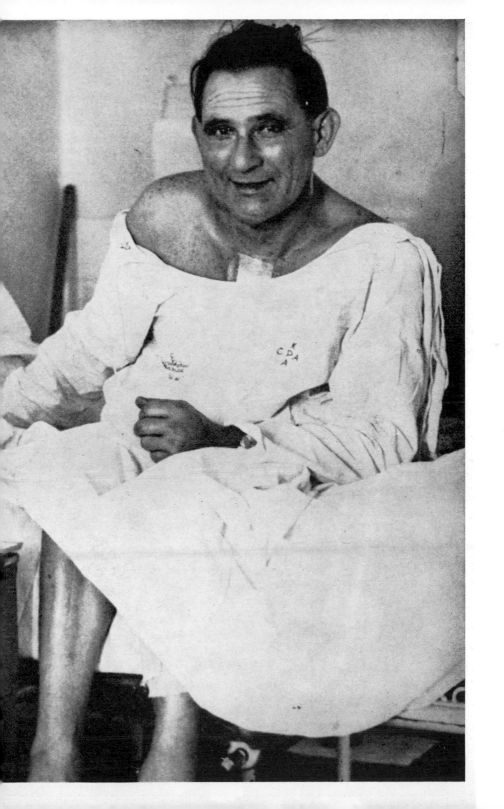

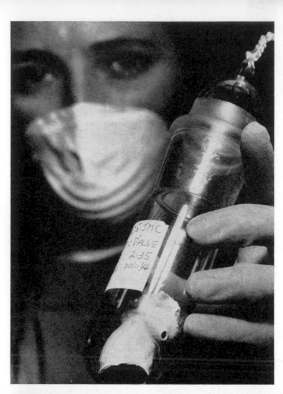

Plate 35. Vacuum flask containing a freeze-dried human heart valve. When soaked in a solution of penicillin it will regain its former texture and properties

Plate 36. Dissection of a human cadaver heart to remove the valves and prepare them for storage, at the National Heart Hospital in London

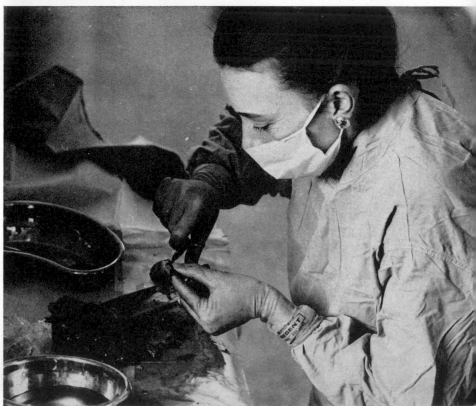

Plate 37. Hyperbaric perfusion unit developed by Dr Ian Hopkinson in Vickers Research Laboratories for the storage of living organs

Plate 38. Glass enclosure, inside which hip prostheses are implanted, at the Wrightington Hospital's Department of Hip Surgery

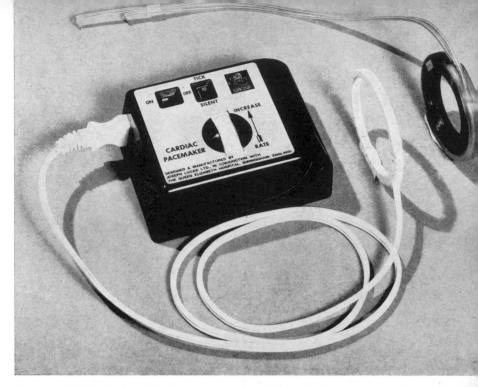

Plate 39. British design of cardiac pacemaker, using a radio-frequency coupling. It is possi
to switch on a reassuring tick when needed

Plate 40. The moonface that develops with long-term treatment with corticosteroids char
terizes this group of kidney recipients. They are ex-patients of St Mary's Hospital in Lon

Mears of the University of Cambridge, having examined 31 alloys, concluded that 'stainless steels (even of the higher chromium-nickel quality) and nickel alloys are unlikely to resist all break-down by pitting when exposed to the body fluids ... indefinitely.'[12]

Happily, these metallurgists found that the cobalt alloys, which are very widely used today for implants, 'may well withstand such exposure for a very long time'. These alloys, of which Vitallium and Vinertia, composed chiefly of cobalt and chromium, and perhaps the best known, are hard and strong (and fairly heavy). They are normally cast very accurately to make such parts as the all-metal hip joint we shall meet later.

One further and fortuitous advantage of these cobalt alloys came to light in 1966. A NASA laboratory, the Lewis Research Center in Cleveland, announced that their atomic arrangement, which is cubic, made them specially satisfactory in situations where rubbing parts are difficult to lubricate, or lubrication breaks down easily, as in an artificial joint (see Plate 28). Normally engineers have preferred metals with a hexagonal atomic arrangement, for they tend to be stronger.

Indeed, it is to the aerospace industry that surgeons should look for their metallic implants in future, for once again the two have requirements in common — perhaps most succinctly stated as a need for the greatest strength and structural integrity for the least weight. Titanium and its alloys, already developed to the point where the world's most advanced airliner, the Boeing S.S.T., will largely be built from it, also emerge with high commendation from the corrosion studies by Hoar and Mears. Titanium offers the strength of steel at about half its weight, and can be alloyed to obtain the cubic structure just mentioned, if required to replace a joint.

Other strong and corrosion-resistant materials that have become available in a state of purity, and in considerable quantity, as a consequence of the needs of aerospace, include tantalum (a very heavy metal), niobium and molybdenum, and their alloys. Specially strengthened ceramics are also being explored.

More intriguing, although further away, is the possibility of using the composite materials now being developed which, by 'gluing' together very strong fibres — of carbon for example — offer immense strength and 'stiffness' for very little weight; and perhaps more important, a structure that more closely approximates to bone, at least in its ability to absorb shock.

Given materials that will withstand satisfactorily the physical and chemical stresses, the surgeon must still design his replacement or repair according to acceptable engineering principles. Yet some of the 'repairs' perpetrated by surgeons one can scarcely imagine being made by the most amateur carpenter. The engineer who can collaborate with a talented surgeon has a tremendous contribution to make in an area where most surgeons are out of their depth and vulnerable. The testy response by one surgeon — 'You try aligning something in the dark hole I've got to work in' — to his collaborator's remark that the metallic knee he'd just made would need some careful aligning when installed, epitomizes the difficulties this new technology can throw up.

The surgeon is also helped by recent efforts to standardize at least the bits and pieces commonly used in orthopaedic surgery. In Britain, for example, British Standard Specification 3531 :1962 specifies the basic requirements for metal surgical implants of stainless steel, cobalt-chromium alloy and titanium. It lays down the dimensions of surgical bone plates, and the size and shape of screws needed to secure them. Eventually one might hope to see the specification embrace an entire system of spare skeletal parts (the drawings already exist in Britain for a complete system of the long bones of the body).

Reconstruction of a skeleton damaged by accident or disease is not exotic surgery but, in the words of one scientist, 'almost a technical service, and often very good value'. Artificial limbs are expensive attachments, as we saw in the last chapter, and still fall far short of the real thing. If by substituting a length of metal or a man-made joint the surgeon can restore the limb to its original usefulness the value to the patient is immense, while there will be no need to replace the prosthesis every couple of years.

Plate 29 shows a knee joint of cobalt-chromium alloy that was implanted by British surgeons in a young woman in 1954. So far as these surgeons at the Institute of Orthopaedics in London are aware, no artificial joint has outlived this one. The woman, who now has two children, is able to walk up to six miles a day. She uses no stick and suffers no pain.

One of the best examples of reconstructive surgery upon the

skeleton, which also serves to illustrate some of the points I have already made on the choice of materials, is found in the artificial hip joint. Unlike heart disease, arthritis (inflammation of a joint) is rarely a killer, but it possibly accounts for far more human misery. According to a World Health Organization survey, the disease costs Britain 30 million working days a year, and there is no real cure. Sometimes relief can be achieved only by fusing the joint, locking it solid, but the inconvenience in cases where for instance both hip joints are afflicted would be intolerable. Since the Second World War, however, it has been possible to excise an arthritic hip or knee joint and replace it with an artificial one.

The hip joint is a ball-and-socket arrangement, the ball of which is an almost perfect hemisphere of 180 degrees that fits into a socket (acetabulum) of virtually the same shape. It has great freedom of movement, in up to three planes simultaneously. The mating surfaces of the joint are coated with a film of cartilage, and the whole joint is enveloped by a membrane, the synovial membrane, exuding synovial fluid, the purpose of which is the supply of nutrients and lubrication to the joint.

This joint absorbs impacts of several hundred pounds per square inch, at the rate of a million or more a year. In walking a mile we place almost our full weight on each joint about a thousand times. Its substitution by an artificial joint is a major piece of reconstructive surgery that, until recently, has been undertaken at considerable risk to the patient, because of the inadequacy of the surgeon's knowledge both of the joint's function and the behaviour of implanted materials. The Stanmore total hip replacement is a consequence of careful attention to both aspects.

It was developed at the Institute of Orthopaedics at Stanmore near London, whose Department of Bio-medical and Surgical Materials has brought together, with enormous success, orthopaedic surgeons and lubrication engineers seconded by a large oil company (British Petroleum). The prosthesis replaces the femoral head and acetabulum — the ball-and-socket — although it can also be made part of a more extensive prosthesis.

The joint, which costs about eighty pounds, is made wholly of metal, cobalt-chromium alloy, in two parts: a cup that is cemented into the pelvis, and a head that is cemented into the femur. The inner surface of the cup, instead of matching the shape

147

of the head, has a concave horseshoe bearing surface, found by calculation and trial to assist the entry of lubricating fluids by a self-pumping process that engineers are trying to apply elsewhere; and at the same time it provides an exit for any particles of metal produced by wear.

Mr Ian Duff-Barclay of British Petroleum, the engineer associated with the development of this hip joint, also devised a means for simulating the human gait, to life-test his prostheses. The human gait pattern is composed essentially of a support phase, beginning when the heel is set to the ground and ending when the big toe leaves it, and a swing phase that begins as the leg starts to swing forward and ends when the heel again touches the ground. The simulator reproduces this cycle, allowing prostheses to be tested continuously under 'walking' loads of up to 300 pounds, with blood plasma providing the lubrication.

British surgeons believe they now lead the world in this branch of reconstructive surgery. In addition to the Stanmore total hip joint, ball-and-socket hip joints have been designed by Mr Peter Ring, consultant orthopaedic surgeon at Redhill General Hospital, also of cobalt-chromium alloy; and by Dr John Charnley at the Wrightington Hospital near Wigan, who uses a head of stainless steel seated in a socket of high-density polyethylene. Charnley, who runs what is virtually a hip hospital, now numbers his patients in thousands.

On a visit to Japan in 1967 I found a clear acrylic reinforced by a high-grade stainless steel being used extensively for artificial joints. The Jikei joint, as it is known, was developed about 1952 by Professor Katayama of the Jikei School of Medicine in Tokyo, and consists of a stainless structure totally encapsulated in '100 per cent pure' acrylic. The surgeon X-rays both the affected and the corresponding normal joint of his patient, using a scale on the film. The proportions are constant and a two-dimensional picture gives enough data to make the repair, unless damage is very extensive. Japanese surgeons now have available 'off the shelf' a full range of joints—hip, shoulder, knee, elbow (see Plates 30 and 31).

Although, as mentioned earlier, plans have been drawn up for a complete set of long bones for the body, the sort of request an engineering workshop may get from the surgeon is pretty imprecise at present. As one engineer has said, a few days before an operation the surgeon will say, 'I'm going to remove this man's knee and about three inches of bone on either side.' With luck he has had a rule or calipers included on the X-ray. There is then a crash programme to knock up a new joint, leaving enough adjustment for anything the surgeon may find when he opens his patient's leg.

It is now technically possible to replace an entire femur, hip joint and knee joint. Plate 32 shows such a structure, composed of a total hip joint of cobalt-chromium alloy, attached to a femoral shaft of titanium, which in turn carries a titanium knee joint fitted with a hinge bearing of cobalt-chromium. The implant was assembled for a patient with an extensive lesion of the femur. In the event, the surgeons found only the upper half of the structure was required. It was attached to the lower part of the patient's femur by an intramedullary pin and grouted into the bone with cement. By the spring of 1968 the implant, developed by the Institute of Orthopaedics in London, had served the patient satisfactorily for over two years.

THE ARTIFICIAL GLAND

Dr Edmond Dewan, famed for his experiments, mentioned earlier, in controlling the alpha rhythm of the brain, tells me of a conversation he had with the late Norbert Wiener, who held that, strange as it may sound, we may some day have prosthetic glands that will use a feedback to supply bodily chemicals as they are needed. Such a mechanism would open the way to mimicry of the body's chemical factories—the biochemical organs like the liver, the pancreas and the endocrine glands.

Some years ago an Australian scientist developed the Rose osmotic pressure pump capsule,[13] an ingenious syringe that can be preset to inject a drug or chemical at some chosen rate, as little as one-hundredth of a millilitre a day (a single drop is about one-tenth of a millilitre). This device can be totally implanted. The capsule contains a small volume of a dye, Congo red, in a rubber sac that is partly collapsed. This sac is separated from another, containing water, by a semi-permeable membrane. Under the pressure of osmosis, water passes through the membrane, slowly increasing the pressure within the rubber sac. It is this pressure that squeezes the chemical from a third, adjoining compartment.

The rate of administration of the chemical will depend on the properties of the membrane—its thickness and surface area, for example. By combining it with microminiature sensing devices, such as means of measuring blood pressure, or pH value, the necessary 'feedback' of information could be established to allow the capsule to control the rate continuously.

Still more elegant is a technique known as micro-encapsulation, in which fluids or solids are sealed inside plastic capsules that may be as small as a few micrometres across. Micro-encapsulation is the secret of 'carbonless' carbon paper, which is paper coated with minuscule capsules full of ink, released when they are crushed by a pen or typewriter key. Many ingenious methods are now known for encapsulating in plastic a great variety of substances, including drugs, such as the relatively long-acting analgesic containing a mixture of microcapsules of the same contents but differing in the solubility of the capsule itself. One particular cold 'cure' that works in this way is said to be effective for twelve hours, but much longer periods of medication are foreseen by some workers.

Judah Folkman and David M. Long at the U.S. Naval Medical Research Institute in Bethesda have experimented with the idea of 'drip-feeding' a chemical stimulant to pace the heart, using such drugs as tri-iodothyronine, isoproterenol, digitoxin and E.D.T.A. They encapsulated these drugs in silicone rubber sacs about a tenth of an inch long.[14]

In essence, their scheme relies on the discovery that many materials, fat-soluble ones in particular, dissolve in the silicone to form a solid solution, usually at an extremely low concentration. This happens when the chemical is encapsulated within its sac. When the sac is buried in living tissues, the body fluids slowly leach the chemical from the outer layers, so that more must dissolve to restore the equilibrium. In this way a very slow and very constant release is sustained; one that depends not on the porosity of the silicone membrane, which can easily be altered by becoming choked with body tissues, but on the solubility of the chemical in the silicone rubber. The size of the molecule is not the ruling factor—there are very large molecules which will transfer in this way, and small ones which will not.

An artificial gland buried beneath the skin may also be the

answer to many of the limitations of present-day methods of birth control, an American scientist once told me. Dr Harry Rudel of the Population Council in New York described how such a gland would leak minute amounts of hormone into a woman's bloodstream at a constant rate—for months or even years at a stretch. If the woman then decided she wanted a baby, the gland would simply be removed.

One obvious advantage this would offer over all of today's methods other than the 'spiral', is that it would require positive action to secure conception, rather than to prevent it. The 'spiral' or intra-uterine contraceptive device (I.U.C.D.), to which this also applies but whose mechanism is still not explained, has proved troublesome to many women.

The new contraceptive system on which Dr Rudel is working is altogether more subtle than the 'Pill', from which it derives. Instead of imposing an artificial menstrual cycle, it aims to do no more than slightly shift the hormonal balance. This might be done by injecting a number of very tiny 'pills' beneath the skin, through a needle, so that they dissolve slowly over a long period. In this way protection might be given for, say, a year at a time.

An artificial gland, however, is more sophisticated and probably less likely to cause irritation. This would take the form of a slender capsule of silicone rubber filled with progesterone. The hormone dissolves in the silicone, and is itself dissolved out again by the flow of body fluids, so there is a constant transfer of the capsule's contents into the bloodstream. The capsule would probably be no more than about a millimetre in diameter, so that it could be implanted through a needle, under local anaesthetic. Its length would depend on how long it was required to prevent conception.

This method of contraception has already been tested extensively in rats, hamsters and rabbits, and trials on primates began in 1960. But clinical trials on women must await more information about the performance of capsules, and whether they should be buried in muscle or subcutaneous fat.

Microcapsules can be scaled down still further, to the dimensions of the cell itself, 'building brick' of living tissue. This raises the possibility of preparing an artificial body fluid from a suspension of microcapsules. The great advantage, in the case of blood for instance, could be the absence of any antibody reaction following

151

a transfusion with such a fluid (a subject discussed in more detail in the next chapter).

A Canadian scientist, Professor Thomas Chang of McGill University, has prepared red blood cell haemolysate encapsulated within nylon membranes only three times the thickness of the red blood cell's natural membrane. These membranes are freely permeable to small molecules, though not to larger ones. Unfortunately, other technical difficulties have intervened so far to prevent the use of these capsules in the bloodstream itself. But Chang has used them successfully in a shunt outside the body, bridging an artery and vein. Such a shunt might be used to treat enzyme deficiency diseases through an encapsulated enzyme without invoking an antibody reaction. Another possibility is a miniaturized artificial kidney of the kind sketched in Fig. 20, by the encapsulation of chemicals that remove unwanted protein from blood, but which ordinarily would damage the blood.

CHAPTER FIVE

Man Transplanted

'Life is a partial, continuous, multiform and conditionally interactive, self-realization of the potentialities of atomic electron states.'

Professor J. D. Bernal, F.R.S.

NATURE'S engineering is far more sophisticated than anything man may yet aspire to. One needs to look no further than the capacity of living tissues for self-repair and regeneration; the astonishing degree to which complex systems like the brain and kidneys are microminiaturized; the incredibly efficient feedback mechanisms (homeostasis) that regulate and integrate the performance of every piece of living tissue; or the immense amount of redundancy that has been built into the human body, ready to compensate for temporary or permanent damage.

The ultimate goal of the surgeon must therefore remain to replace or replenish faulty tissue with material no less versatile; which means tissue that was once and preferably still is alive and healthy. In mechanical terms the techniques needed may not be so difficult, and for organs at least seemed largely to be resolved by the turn of the century, through the work of Alexis Carrel, in for example reconnecting major blood vessels and nerves.

But a bio-chemical intolerance soon began to intrude, which to this day has persisted in hindering man's ability to live in harmony with live tissue from a source other than his own body (or that of his identical twin). At best he achieves what one eminent surgeon has called a state of uneasy symbiosis, and this only within the past few years. Ever present, even years later, is the risk of an abrupt biological interaction that will end in the body's rejection of its acquired component.

The surgeon now distinguishes three primary sources of living tissue. There is the *autograft*, which is tissue shifted from one part of the body to another, and which forms the basis of the plastic surgeon's technique. Then there is the *homograft*, of tissue transplanted from one person to another (or, more precisely, between animals of the same species). Thirdly, there is the *heterograft* (now called the *xenograft*), which is tissue transplanted from one species to another, as is the case when a pig's heart valve is used to replace a human one ravaged by rheumatic fever.

The autografting of tissue has a surprisingly long history. Susruta, the Hippocrates of Hindu surgery, was performing autografts to reconstruct damaged noses and correct deformities of the ear lobe in the sixth and seventh centuries B.C. His technique remains to this day one of the basic practices of the plastic surgeon: to cut a pedicle or flap of skin from the cheek of his patient and, leaving one end still attached to the cheek, stitch the other in place to restore the defect. The tissue is left like this until accepted at the new site.

The same procedure was adopted during the fifteenth century by the Branca family in Sicily, to repair a nose, using tissue from the patient's arm, which had thus to be strapped close to his face. As recently as 1963, Dr Joseph E. Murray, Chief Plastic Surgeon of the Peter Bent Brigham Hospital in Boston, used the Branca technique on a visit to India, to restore the features of a Hindu woman whose nose had been cut off as a punishment.

Not until the nineteenth century was skin freely autografted in the sense of being cut off completely from its blood supply and removed to another part of the body. Even today, however, it is rarely transplanted successfully. One of the most valuable consequences of a solution to tissue rejection would be the prospect of transplanting skin to repair bad burns.

Blood, however, had been successfully transplanted — transfused — two centuries earlier. Blood transfusion will probably turn out to be a prototype in certain important respects, such as matching and storage, for far more sophisticated transplanting processes, and on this count alone its transfusion is of special significance.

Blood is one of the connective tissues of the body and it provides the body with its primary system of transportation. It is quite simple to tap this system and moreover a healthy person can part with about a pint with no effect worse than a passing dizziness. The body is continually manufacturing fresh blood and it can replace a pint within twenty-four hours. Here, then, is one transplantable tissue that can be kept in prime condition virtually until it is needed.

As long ago as 1615, Andreas Libavius proposed the transfusion of blood by 'cannulation of the arteries of donor and recipient with silver tubes'; although it is doubtful whether he actually carried out the procedure. Half a century later, in 1666, the Oxford anatomist Richard Lower bled a dog almost to the point of death, then replenished its blood supply from another dog. Within months of this experiment, in July 1667, a transfusion of a lamb's blood was made by a Parisian professor, Jean Denis, to a boy of fifteen who had been bled a score of times in the course of being treated for a fever. The boy survived his xenograft of nine ounces of blood with nothing worse than a burning pain along his arm.

A subsequent patient of Denis was less fortunate, and the technique fell into disrepute until early in the nineteenth century. In 1818, a London obstetrician, James Blundell, gave the first transfusion between humans to a man who was dying of a stomach cancer. Although this patient died, Blundell was more successful with patients who had lost blood heavily during childbirth, using a two-way syringe to transfer the blood.[1]

But uncertainties confounded the transfusion of blood right until the turn of the century, when Karl Landsteiner and others distinguished the major blood groups, and showed how the mixing of blood from different groups can sometimes cause the agglutination or clumping together of red blood cells and consequent breakdown of the tissue. We now know the matching of blood groups to be a key factor in tissue transplantation.

Four main blood groups: O, A, B and AB are distinguished in this way. But they are not uniformly distributed among mankind — which helps to account for the higher success rate in transfusion before their discovery than might be expected from the law of averages. For example, 42 per cent of Britons possess blood of group A, and can receive without harm transfusions of blood of either group A or group O (46 per cent). Those possessing blood

155

of group AB, on the other hand, although comprising only 3 per cent of mankind, can accept blood from any of the four groups. Among Britons there is about one chance in four of a serious reaction if the blood is not matched.

A further complication is the blood group factors, of which the best known is the so-called Rhesus factor, discovered in 1940. In the case of one very rare blood factor, there are only nine known cases in the entire world.

If blood is to be stored against an emergency it needs a preservative to prevent putrefaction, that can lead for example to a liver infection and jaundice. The first was sodium citrate, discovered just in time for the First World War, when the British Army established the first blood banks. By the Second World War a further advance in the preservation of blood, whereby it was drawn into acid citrate solution then topped up with a solution of dextrose, kept it stable enough to be parachuted into the front line. According to Dr Gordon Wolstenholme, director-general of the C.I.B.A. Foundation, about 10 per cent of the wounded of this war were transfused, receiving up to 40 pints of blood for every 100 wounded, together with 30 pints of blood plasma.[2]

Donated blood can be kept in prime condition for about 21 days, but nevertheless, wastage is relatively slight, about 7 per cent according to one estimate. But the 21-day limit on the life of whole blood can raise difficulties in stockpiling against an emergency such as warfare or an earthquake. According to one report, there was an enormous volume donated and wasted in the U.S.A. in the days preceding the Cuban missile crisis.

The war in Vietnam has helped to stimulate interest in the deep-freezing of blood to preserve it for months or even years. The starting point here was the discovery, in Britain, that bull sperm could be preserved alive if glycerol were added as an 'anti-freeze' before it was frozen. In 1950, Dr Audrey Smith of the National Institute for Medical Research showed that glycerol could also prevent the rupture by ice crystals of red blood cells. There remained, however, the problem of removing the glycerol once the blood had been thawed out again.

Several machines have now been developed in American laboratories that can reconstitute the blood in a matter of minutes, one being the Huggins Cytoglomerator, developed at Harvard

Medical School. These machines are expensive, which places a premium on each pint of blood preserved in this way, but the cost may be acceptable for the storage of rare blood groups. More recently a method of preserving blood using extremely rapid rates of freezing to $-80°$ C, assisted by a preservative, poly-vinyl-pyrolidine, that remains outside the cells, has been developed at the British Army Blood Supply Depot at Aldershot.

One tissue structure which appears to be largely independent of problems of compatibility—for reasons we shall return to later—is the cornea, the transparent 'window' of the eye. As long ago a 1905 the Viennese surgeon Zirm reported the successful grafting of a cornea on to a man whose eyes had been burned by quick-lime, using tissue from a young boy obliged to lose an eye. Half a century later a Russian ophthalmologist, V. P. Filatov, laid the foundations of modern keratoplasty (surgery on the cornea) with his techniques for removing complete sections of the cornea and transplanting them, and also for storing corneas.

Today, corneal transplants enjoy an excellent record of success; a record to which antibiotics, the anti-inflammatory cortico-steroids and new instruments have all made their contribution. In a report to the C.I.B.A. Foundation's symposium on 'Ethics in Medical Progress' in 1966, the late Mr P. V. Ryecroft discussed a series of a hundred (unselected) corneal transplants at one English hospital, which had 'an overall success rate of 78 per cent', with 'marked visual improvement' in forty-eight cases.

It is believed that there are about 4 million people in the world today who are blind (but need not be), in consequence of accident, disease or burns. In perhaps 5 per cent of these cases the damage is too great for a living graft to take, and a plastic implant would be needed. But in the great majority of cases homografts of living tissue could restore sight at least partially. To this end tissue banks have been established in the past few years, notably the International Eye Bank in Washington and the (much smaller) Eye Bank in East Grinstead near London, which supply living tissue throughout the world. These banks are undoubtedly the fore-runners of tissue banks of far wider inventory, once the difficulties of continuously perfusing an organ with fresh blood are overcome.

It needs perhaps to be emphasized here that although everyone talks loosely of eyes and eye banks, the surgeon is concerned only

157

with the cornea, about three-fifths of an inch thick and one-sixth of the eye's volume. There is no possibility of grafting a whole eye — essentially an extension of the nerve tissue of the brain itself — in the foreseeable future.

Several obstacles still hamper the restoration of sight by corneal grafts, especially in those parts of the world — such as the Middle East — where disease is the principal cause. The most important is religious and superstitious prejudice concerning the sanctity of the eyes. Many Israelis and Arabs, for example, will accept corneal grafts but will not donate them. Elsewhere, as in India and Japan, there is little enthusiasm for either, despite the enormous need. Facilities, too, are often inadequate for an operation that requires the patient to remain in hospital under close observation for three to six weeks.

One of the latest corneal techniques is the work of an Italian surgeon, Professor Benedetto Strampelli, of St John's Hospital, Rome, who has ingeniously combined the autograft with the inert plastic implant in his *odonto-kerato-prosthesis*. The idea here is to cut a cross-section from the root of a tooth from the same patient, and to use this collar as the 'frame' within which to cement a tiny plastic window. This structure is then implanted within the cornea. Essentially this is a 'last-ditch' technique, for use in cases where the patient has rejected more orthodox grafts. But it can provide the patient with at least a pin-hole of high-grade vision, and can be done moreover without the tooth itself being removed.

Another ingenious technique, described to the second International Corneo-Plastic Conference in London in 1967 by a Columbian surgeon, Dr José Barraquer of Bogota, aims to correct gross errors of focusing by removing and reshaping the patient's cornea, so to avoid the need for especially strong spectacles. A thin layer is sliced from the cornea, frozen to harden it, then ground on a lathe — much as a contact lens is fashioned. Then it is stitched back in place. The technique, called keratomileusis, is held to have special relevance in countries where contact lenses have not yet been fully developed.

PROTOTYPE 'SPARE PART'

Hitherto, we have discussed what can be called simple transplants, in so far as they invoke no bio-chemical intolerance to any great degree. This is not the case when we come to consider the grafting of organs.

Medical interest in transplantation is strongest today in the case of the kidney—the prototype 'spare part', as it has been called. There are a number of reasons for this: one being the high mortality among relatively young people from kidney disease. Another is the fact that since this organ is paired and the body can fully adjust in a few weeks to working with a single kidney (two-thirds of a kidney can cope, in fact), there is—potentially—a plentiful supply of spare parts. It is also very easy to assess kidney function.

The most important reasons, however, as I have already outlined, are the success of the artificial kidney in restoring dying patients to a state of health and fitness where the major operation of a kidney transplantation can be condoned; and the insurance it offers should the surgeon find himself unable to control the immunological response to the graft. He has no such insurance in the case of the heart, lungs or liver.

The kidney is a small, bean-shaped organ ten centimetres in length and weighing 120 to 150 grams, shrouded in fat to protect it from damage. Its three connections with the rest of the body, the renal artery and vein (sometimes paired) and the ureter that carries urine into the bladder, are all substantial vessels, convenient for the surgeon to handle, and the transplant technique is well within the skills of any surgeon familiar with vascular surgery. By the turn of the century, Dr Alexis Carrel had perfected the technique of suturing the vessels and hence of physically transplanting the organ in animals.

What he had not overcome, he was later to learn, was the immunological barrier, which has completely frustrated the surgeon until quite recently. Even today, this barrier is by no means surmounted, and the transplanted organ normally survives only through the suppression of certain natural bio-chemical processes.

The first successful transplantation of a kidney in man was performed on December 23rd, 1954, when a kidney donated by his identical twin brother Ronald was sewn into the abdomen of twenty-three-year-old Richard Herrick of Northboro, Massachusetts. The operation, performed by Dr Joseph Murray at the Peter Bent Brigham Hospital,[3] soon restored Richard's health to normal. He married, had two children and lived another eight years. Nor was his twin to suffer from the loss of a kidney.

Twins are comparatively common, one in eighty of all births, but identical (monozygotic) twins, where both develop from the same fertilized egg, are more scarce, only a fifth of all twins. In 1959 Dr Murray and Dr J. P. Merrill claimed a further success, this time with the transference of a kidney between twins who were not identical.[4] But this transplant required the most drastic of measures to prolong the union of tissues.

It is well-known that one of the most serious consequences of exposure to ionizing radiation is that it weakens the body's natural resistance to infection. In this case the surgeons administered a near-lethal dose of X-rays, deliberately to suppress the immuno-logical response and allow the new kidney to 'take'.

That same year, 1959, another method for suppressing the immunological response was announced, the first of the so-called immuno-suppressive' agents, 6-mercaptopurine, soon followed by azathioprine, a related but safer preparation. Azathioprine, how-ever, is normally given with a steroid, and this renders the patient vulnerable to infection, even from organisms normally residing harmlessly within his body. How these drugs work is still not fully understood, but the remarkable success in the past year or two with kidney transplants can largely be attributed to the surgeon's success in establishing a suitable immuno-suppressive regime based on azathioprine for the recipient; a precarious balance between the mechanisms of rejection on the one hand, and infec-tion and/or toxicity on the other.

The first step in a kidney transplantation is to secure a new kidney — no easy matter, as we shall see. There is no doubt that the greatest chance of success so far lies in exchanges between close (blood) relatives, the closer the better, which limits the availability and introduces moral complications, for example when one member of a family is coerced by others into donating an organ. When a volunteer donor is available, however, the two operations for excision and transplantation can be conducted together, in adjoining operating theatres, with minimal risk to the organ itself provided its blood supply is restored within about an hour.

A more plentiful source would be cadavers, but it is necessary to remove the organ as rapidly as possible, within a few minutes, lest it be damaged by deprivation of a supply of oxygenated blood and the putrefaction that follows. Nor, once removed, is there any way yet of storing the organ for longer than a few hours. So the patient must be maintained in readiness for a major operation at very short notice, as soon as a suitable kidney becomes available.

Most people who die in hospital are not, in fact, suitable donors, because of their age or the infections, diseases or damage from which they are suffering. The terminal stages of life can also wreak havoc with the kidneys.

But one satisfactory source could be those who die from brain damage, estimated by Nathan P. Couch, director of the Blood Bank at the Peter Bent Brigham Hospital, to be good for some 10,600 kidneys a year in the U.S.A. This compares with about 7,600 potential kidney recipients a year (only a fraction of those suffering from kidney disease are considered suitable recipients). Couch carried out a statistical survey of supply and demand for new kidneys and livers, from which he concluded that 'efficient logistic techniques and legal codes should make it possible for all transplanted kidneys and livers to be harvested from the recently deceased.'[5]

Animal cadavers are another prospect, for at least they avoid the unsavoury prospect of the surgeon poised, vulture-like, over a dying person ready to remove his kidneys within minutes of death. But the immunological barrier to tissue acceptance of another species promises to be even more difficult to surmount.

Once parted from its blood supply there is difficulty in sustaining a kidney in prime condition. For this reason, the blood of a dying donor may be kept flowing and oxygenated by machine after death has occurred, until the surgeon is ready to excise the organ. If it is then to be transported from one hospital to another, the organ is literally kept on ice, in a vessel filled with oxygen under pressure.

The transplantation itself takes no more than two to three hours—and indeed must be done as quickly as possible, with the blood supply restored within an hour. The patient meanwhile will have already been started on a regime of immuno-suppressive drugs, such as azathioprine together with a corticosteroid such as prednisone.

How successful the surgeon has been in restoring renal function

L

can soon be judged from the volume and quality of the urine the patient excretes. With cadaver kidneys, however, it is not uncommon for a couple of weeks to pass before renal function is restored, during which time the recipient is maintained on artificial dialysis. Similarly, should the surgeon find that he is losing the battle against the immunological response—and an attempt at rejection almost always occurs in the first few weeks—he can revert to the machine and remove the new organ before the increasing dosage of drugs puts the recipient excessively at risk.

The recipient is nursed under conditions of the utmost sterility for at least the first few days, since his natural resistance to infection has virtually been paralysed. Should his immunological defences attempt, nonetheless, to reject the transplant, the interaction may manifest itself either insidiously with a slow deterioration of renal function, or abruptly, precipitating an acute rejection crisis. Either way, the risk to the acquired organ is considerable; hence the need to keep the patient under the closest surveillance, in readiness to make swift changes in the regime of immunosuppressant drugs, and to administer a powerful antibiotic to counter the growing hazard from infection as the dose is increased.

According to Professor Roy Calne of Cambridge, a pioneer in kidney transplantation, the longer a patient goes without rejecting the transplant, the less likelihood there will be of catastrophic rejection. But rejection may still occur months, even years after the operation. This is one of the more frustrating and inexplicable aspects of kidney, and indeed of all organ transplantation.

In Boston there is a Registry of Human Kidney Transplants that collates records on kidney transplantations throughout the world. A successful transplant is usually acknowledged today to be one that survives for more than a year. (Remember, the drug azathioprine that will successfully control the immune reaction has been generally available only since 1964.) The latest figures indicate that a patient today has at least a 60 to 70 per cent chance of a successful union with a kidney that comes from a blood relative, and a 50 per cent chance with a cadaver kidney; although one or two surgeons, notably Starzl in the U.S. and Calne at Cambridge, have records that are very much better.

Properly prepared, under optimum conditions, a recipient can now hope to survive that 'state of uneasy symbiosis' for an average of two to three years, and nearer three than two. But plainly it remains necessary to plan for repeat transplants, with the artificial kidney held in readiness to tide the patient over periods of crisis.

Many surgeons now believe it unlikely that the recipient of an organ will ever be free from the need to take immuno-suppressive measures. Professor Sir Michael Woodruff of the Department of Surgical Science in Edinburgh, another pioneer in the transplanting of kidneys, experienced the case of a boy who received one of his father's kidneys, and whose intake of immuno-suppressants had been reduced over a period of five years to a very low level. But within three weeks of discontinuing the regime of drugs altogether the boy suffered a sharp rejection crisis.

The long-term solution to this inconvenience may well be the implantable plastic 'gland', of the kind discussed earlier, that leaks enough of the drug into the bloodstream to keep the graft under control. Such a gland may need replenishing no more frequently than once a year.

Professor Woodruff is a confirmed believer in the close integration of artificial dialysis and transplantation techniques. 'When the patient has reached the peak of improvement on dialysis,' he told a meeting of science writers in London in November 1967, 'he should be persuaded to accept a transplant, for the patient who is doing well on a transplant is incomparably better off.' Successful as artificial dialysis has undoubtedly been, there are some functions the artificial kidney cannot restore. With a transplant the patient is not only free from the machine but is more alert, has more stamina—feels 'cleaner'. Nevertheless, the patient's place on the artificial kidney cannot be filled until the transplant is truly established, four or six weeks at least; while there must obviously be enough slack in the system to permit the patient to return to artificial dialysis at short notice even years later.

WHAT PREVENTS ACCEPTANCE?

What, then, is the nature of the so-called immunological response, the barrier that proves such a hindrance to surgeons working in one of the most exciting areas of medical practice? It is in fact the body's natural biological defence against foreign protein; beautifully simple in concept, but immensely difficult to unravel and circumvent. So far, as we have seen in the case of the kidney

163

transplants, success in cases other than transplantation between identical twins has been at the risk of gravely weakening the patient against all kinds of infection, including attack by organisms that normally live quite harmlessly in our lungs and elsewhere. Such an organism caused the death of the first recipient of a human heart, in 1967.

Many attempts were made in the Middle Ages to transplant living tissue from one person to another, the donor in most cases being a slave or servant of the household. So coercion in this context is no new development! Unfortunately, the homograft invariably failed to take, an observation that inspired Samuel Butler to comment sardonically in *Hudibras* (1663) :

> So learned Taliacotius from
> The brawny part of Porter's bum
> Cut supplemental Noses, which
> Would last as long as Parent breech:
> But when the last Date of Nock was out,
> Off dropt the Sympathetick Snout.

Learned Taliacotius was none other than the celebrated Italian surgeon Gaspare Tagliacozzi (1554–99), now acknowledged as the 'father' of plastic surgery (although the term 'plastic' was not to emerge until the nineteenth century). Tagliacozzi believed rejection to be due to what he called the 'force and power of individuality'; which, even if it doesn't explain anything, seems a pretty accurate way of putting it. We now explain it as the body's ability to distinguish between 'self' and 'not-self'.

It was not until 1937 that the evidence was forthcoming that it is the body's own defences that reject tissues from all but the most closely related sources. In that year the late Dr Peter Gorer, a British authority on immunology, found that antibodies have a role in the rejection. Antibodies are chemicals the body generates specifically to neutralize antigens — anything the body distinguishes as 'not-self'.

Soon after, in 1943, a Scottish surgeon, Dr Tom Gibson, and an English biologist, Dr (now Sir) Peter Medawar, engaged in the repair of bad burns received by servicemen, published a paper entitled 'The fate of skin homografts in man', in which they recorded their attempts to homograft skin on to an animal that had already rejected a graft from the same source.[6] The second rejection, they found, was much swifter and more emphatic than the first.

This led to the idea, subsequently pursued with great success by Medawar, of the 'second set' reaction, where the first attempt at a graft is believed to alert the body's own defence mechanism. Antibodies are synthesized and circulated in the bloodstream ready to combat the next intrusion by the same antigens. This of course is the basis of immunization with vaccines against such diseases as smallpox or influenza; and also the reason why a person who has once had a disease such as measles is unlikely to suffer it severely, if at all, ever again.

In other words, some measure of control of the immune response had proved possible—and if it could be 'turned up' there was always the likelihood it could be 'turned down'.

In 1960 Dr Peter Medawar and an Australian scientist, Sir F. Macfarlane Burnet of the Royal Melbourne Hospital, shared the Nobel Prize for Medicine for 'their discovery of acquired immunological tolerance'; a discovery that opened up once again the prospects for organ transplantation.

One source of the body's defences is the lymphatic system, a network of fine vessels that irrigate the tissues with a fluid— lymph—similar in composition to blood plasma. This fluid eventually drains back into the veins. Scattered throughout the network are small glands known as lymph nodes, up to an inch across, wherein the battle against invasion by foreign protein, from bacteria and viruses to complete organs, appears to be joined. Those lymph nodes, the source of the lymphocytes or white cells (see Fig. 24), that are close to the surface, such as those in the groin or beneath the arm, may become enlarged and tender in the course of fighting an infection of the adjoining tissues.

Perhaps the most important consequence of the entire effort on transplantation so far is the work it has inspired on immunology. But discoveries on this front will, it is hoped, come full circle in affording the surgeon more effective methods of suppressing the immunological response just enough to permit the union of genetically different tissues, yet not so much as to endanger unduly the defences of the recipient.

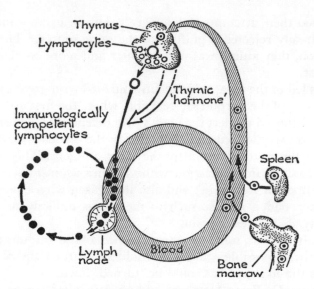

FIG. 24. The role of the thymus in conferring immunity

We can now distinguish four conditions under which a transplant will survive. The first concerns those tissues, such as the cornea of the eye and the valves of the heart, that are free from blood or lymph vessels and so largely inaccessible to the antibodies these fluids are transporting.

Another is when the transplant is placed in a specially favourable position such as the anterior chamber of the eye or the white matter of the brain, when either its capacity to immunize the recipient or its accessibility to immunologically active recipient cells is reduced. A foetus, incidentally, normally has antigens that derive from the father which are lacking in the mother, but survives gestation because the placenta does not allow the passage of cells between the two bloodstreams.

There is a third condition of survival when the donor possesses no antigens that are lacking in the recipient. For all practical purposes, at present, this is the case only when the donor and recipient are identical twins; although intensive inbreeding for many generations might also yield the desired result. Theoretically, of course, this could happen by chance between unrelated donor and recipient, but the contingency is a remote one, and could be made less so only through far more precise methods of

166

tissue typing than we have at present, together with large banks of tissue from which to select.

The fourth condition of survival depends on the recipient's capacity to react immunologically being reduced, either through disease or artificially. For example, ionizing radiation such as X-rays or gamma-rays will suppress the immunological response. One of the hazards of over-exposure to radiation is that it leaves the body vulnerable to infection. But irradiation of the lymph nodes and of the graft itself, under very careful control, formed an important part of the early immuno-suppressive regimes developed by a number of surgeons for the transplantation of kidneys.

The other part of the regime was the administration of drugs, of which there are now several possible kinds. The earliest, known as alkylating agents and including the now generally used azathioprine and others used in the treatment of cancer, behave in much the same way as radiation, by inhibiting cell division and proliferation, and hence the synthesis of new tissue. It is a mechanism that relates closely to the immune response.

IMMUNO-SUPPRESSION

The rapid progress made in kidney grafting in the past five years is due above all to azathioprine, discovered by Dr George Hitchings and his colleagues in the Tuckahoe, New York, laboratories of Burroughs Wellcome.[7] Virtually every organ transplant patient since 1963, when the rush really began, has received a daily dose of azathioprine (Imuran). The regime applied to heart and liver recipients is basically that worked out initially to control kidney grafts. Typically, it costs about seventy-two pounds a year to maintain a kidney recipient on this drug.

A regime has been evolved by the leading transplant surgeons that requires the administration of azathioprine and a synthetic steroid such as prednisone or prednisolone. Given together, these drugs have a synergistic effect, and are more effective in combating the rejection than either drug given alone. Azathioprine, although toxic, does not knock out the recipient's resistance to infection — in fact at the dosage now recommended of 3 milligrams per kilogram of body weight daily, it has proved to be remarkably safe.

Unfortunately, this is not the case with the steroids, which do knock out the body's resistance to infection. This is the component

167

whose dosage is increased at the first hint of rejection; while at the same time a powerful but even more toxic antibiotic, actinomycin C, is given. The steroid is the component the surgeons are most anxious to minimize, for they affect so many of the body's functions. The 'moonface' characteristic of patients on long-term steroid therapy is only the outward manifestation of widespread interference with the body's hormone balance. As one medical authority has observed, 'the most serious complication of steroid therapy is death'.

But there is another, more subtle approach that aims to block the synthesis of some specific, albeit still unidentified, substance concerned with rejection. Involving the use of a serum, it is beginning to attract considerable attention among the world's transplant surgeons. Antilymphocytic serum (A.L.S.) as the immuno-suppressant is called, was a Russian discovery that antedates the Revolution, but it was Woodruff and his colleagues in Edinburgh who in the mid-1960s first showed that the drug worked in preventing graft rejection.

The advantages A.L.S. appears to offer over the drugs on which the entire organ transplant technique has been built up is that there are fewer side effects and far less risk of exposing a recipient to infection. It is also more potent; potent enough, it is hoped, to make the transplanting of skin—the body's first line of defence— possible for the first time. The great expectation for A.L.S. is that it will allow the surgeon to reduce the dose of steroids to far lower levels, and will also eliminate the need for the toxic antibiotic actinomycin C should rejection erupt. Medawar has gone so far as to call it 'the only true immuno-suppressant agent'.

To obtain A.L.S., live human cells (lymphocytes) are injected into animals, where they stimulate an immune reaction and the formation of antibodies that act specifically against themselves. The antiserum, circulating in the animal's blood, is removed and purified, yielding a serum that has been shown to be highly specific in suppressing the lymphocytes responsible for the immune reaction. Just how it works we still do not know, beyond the fact that it appears to put the lymphocytes out of business.

At this stage the serum contains toxic ingredients that will attack the patient's blood cells, and must be carefully purified if serum sickness is to be avoided. But other ingredients, still unidentified,

remain to cause the recipient pain each time the drug is injected —
'your bottom aches and aches', one scientist told me. This is a
serious matter in a drug that must be administered daily.

In other words, despite some spectacular achievements in organ
transplantation that can apparently be attributed, in part at least,
to the serum, it is by no means certain that A.L.S. is the perfect
immuno-suppressant. But it could well point the way to perfection.

TYPING OF TISSUE

We know that human tissue, like blood, has characteristics that
can differ widely from one person to another. But the definition
of the tissue groups — and more particularly those that matter —
has proved much more difficult than for blood. There may be a
score or more of factors, but the hope is that only about six really
matter, and by matching those six the surgeon will obtain a union
of tissues almost as good as the match between identical twins.

The significance of this is best illustrated by the transplanted
kidney, where world statistics indicate that the recipient of a
kidney from his identical twin stands about a 90 per cent chance of
surviving for more than one year, while the recipient of a kidney
from an unrelated donor stands no more than one chance in two.

Clearly, the greater the mismatch between the two tissues, the
more drastic the immuno-suppressive measures likely to be
needed, and the greater the risk — and discomfort — to the recipient.

A Dutch scientist, Dr J. J. van Rood of Leyden University
Hospital, has used a computer to look for the patterns in white
blood cell genes. He has found relationships that correlate remarkably closely with the success or failure of a number of kidney graft
operations. Van Rood has also organized 'Eurotransplant', the
computerized classification of the tissues of Europe's patients on
haemodialysis, to facilitate the location of close-matching donors.

Nevertheless, a 'summit meeting' of heart surgeons in Cape
Town in 1968 concluded that tissue typing was still at the stage
of development reached by blood matching two or three decades
ago. Of the rather primitive tissue typing tests available, those that
use antisera of various kinds to identify antigens by agglutination,
and by the cytotoxic (cell-destroying) effects they produce, seem
to offer the best hope. Others include the third-man skin graft, a
rough screening test that detects immunological differences and

169

similarities, though without actually characterizing the antigens themselves. Skin from the prospective recipient is grafted on to a third person, who thereafter receives skin grafts from a panel of prospective donors. The first donor graft to be rejected would be presumed to share the greatest number of transplantation antigens with the graft from the prospective recipient. A third person is needed for this test to avoid sensitizing the prospective recipient against the graft chosen.

No less important, however, is compatibility between the blood groups of donor and recipient.

Once a satisfactory method has been reached for at least eliminating the more obvious incompatibilities, it should be possible to organize a central catalogue of available tissue, that a computer might swiftly track down when the need arose, much as big airlines now use computers to track down seats on their aircraft.

What we still don't know is how many of the factors can be mismatched before the immunological barrier becomes too great; in other words, how poor a match can the surgeon get away with, and rely on immuno-suppression to maintain the state of uneasy symbiosis for an acceptable period? The point will remain a crucial one, at least until there is an abundance of tissue from which to choose, and perhaps for long after.

HEART, LUNGS AND LIVER?

The relative success recently of the immuno-suppressive measures in the case of the kidney has revived the surgeon's optimism about organ transplantation generally, and today there is widespread discussion within the medical profession itself about the prospects for transplants of the other organs—heart, lungs, liver and so forth.

Unfortunately, none of the other organs enjoys the advantages peculiar to the kidney, notably the existence of a machine to which the patient can be rapidly recoupled should the transplanted organ fail to regain its function right away, or should its function become impaired, for example through a rejection reaction that fails to respond quickly to treatment. What is more, no other organ can be obtained from a living donor—other, that is, than a cerebral cripple whose central nervous system is so seriously damaged that his doctors have decided on euthanasia.

There are, as I have already indicated, four broad areas of

unresolved technical problems of immediate concern to the transplant surgeon. First, the immuno-suppressive measures already outlined are far from perfect, even in the case of the kidney where the surgeon has the insurance of a standby machine. The most widely used drugs carry two grave risks. One is that by paralysing the body's natural defences they will leave it vulnerable to infection even by organisms normally considered benign residing within the recipient's body. The other is that the drug itself will attack some other part of the body, typically the liver, kidneys or lungs — 'transplant lung' is already a recognized syndrome in kidney recipients.

The transplant team treads a tightrope. Too much immuno-suppressant and the body itself is exposed to an overwhelming infection, or to attack by the drug itself; too little, and the body begins to turn on 'itself', on the new graft.

When rejection arises, as it invariably does, the surgeon has only one course of action at present: to administer more immuno-suppressant drugs. In the case of the kidney the experienced surgeon now knows how far he can go without putting his patient unduly at risk. Once that point has been reached he will abandon the transplant, remove the rejected organ and return his patient to the care of the artificial kidney.

There is no such insurance for the recipient of a new heart, lungs or liver. The surgeon has no alternative but to continue his efforts to combat rejection with ever-increasing amounts of the drug.

The other three problem areas, as Fig. 1 indicates, are all intimately related to the limitations of the present immuno-suppressive measures, and hence to the recipient's well-being. One is the matching of tissues, still by no means a precise process, or even a quick one. There is hope — it is no more than that — that by securing the best possible match the surgeon will obtain a union approaching that between identical twins.

Tissue matching is a complex and time-consuming process, and this brings us to the third problem area, the storage of tissues. Ideally, the surgeon requires a machine to which an excised organ can be transferred immediately; one on which he might 'tune' the organ under conditions closely akin to the natural conditions, to help it over the shock of its severance and bring it back into peak condition for transplantation.

171

As we shall see, the first organ storage machines of this kind are only just beginning to appear, and almost no clinical experience has yet been accumulated. The entire process of transplantation, including the matching of tissue, must be performed in great haste; and since there can be no reserve of tissue, the matches will almost inevitably fall short of perfection.

Existing methods of organ storage have one salient weakness which they share with the heart-lung machine: they tend to damage the red cells of the fresh blood they are pumping through the organs in store, which in turn damage the organs. A satisfactory solution to this problem, that would allow organs to be perfused continuously with blood for perhaps forty-eight hours, could also make a significant contribution to the last of the four missing pieces of technology. This is a satisfactory circulatory by-pass—heart-lung machine—which might be used to sustain the recipient of a heart whose graft was failing to respond to immunosuppression.

HEART TRANSPLANTATION

Nevertheless, despite the unresolved technical problems, attempts have been made by a number of surgeons to graft other organs, of which the heart transplants in particular have excited the imagination of the public. The first heart transplant, the ultimate in open-heart surgery, was performed in January 1964.[8]

Dr James D. Hardy of the University of Mississippi Medical Center was preparing to transplant the heart of a man dying of brain damage into the chest of another man dying of heart disease, but the condition of his prospective recipient began to deteriorate rapidly. He grafted instead the heart of a chimpanzee. The transfer itself was accomplished successfully and the xenograft beat strongly for ninety minutes. Then abruptly it stopped, apparently unequal to the task of supporting a full-grown man. In this case the problem of an immunological response would hardly have had time to intrude.

The first human-to-human heart transplantation was performed by a South African surgeon, Professor Christiaan Barnard, in the Groote Schuur Hospital in Cape Town on December 3rd, 1967, when Mr Louis Washkansky, fifty-four, dying of heart disease and also suffering from diabetes, received the heart of Miss Denise

Darvall, twenty-five, who had just died from head injuries after being knocked down by a car.

The girl's father gave permission for her heart to be donated. The tissues of the dead girl and dying man were then matched by the technique of Van Rood and found to be compatible (or, rather, not incompatible: there was direct incompatibility with only one antigen).

The heart team transplanted the bulk of the cardiac tissue, except for the crown, embodying the sinus (S-A) node or natural 'pacemaker', thus leaving intact the nerve connection between the recipient's heart and his brain (see Fig. 25). It was an operative technique worked out by Dr Norman E. Shumway, a Californian surgeon, over the previous seven years, and involved a total of nine reconnections to blood vessels. When some five hours later the donated heart, much smaller at 350 grams than the one grossly dilated by disease that it replaced, had been stitched securely in place, an electric shock was used to restart it.[9]

Within two days Mr Washkansky (see Plate 34), heavily dosed with azathioprine, prednisone and antibiotics to paralyse his body's natural tendency to react to the presence of genetically foreign tissue, and given local radio-cobalt (gamma-ray) treatment of his new graft, was eating solid food and regaling the medical staff with remarks like 'I am the new Frankenstein'. There can be no question that Louis Washkansky was chosen for the central role in this medical drama as much for psychological as purely clinical reasons. But surgeons familiar with transplant surgery were well aware that the first immunological crisis would probably arise between the tenth and fourteenth days. True to form he developed what appeared to be pneumonia on the thirteenth day.

Whether the chirpy South African grocer died on the eighteenth day from double pneumonia, as was reported,[10] or from an overdose of drugs or radiation, or from a rejection reaction on the part of his body as a whole, is really quite irrelevant. He died an uncomfortable death as a consequence of the transplantation and its rejection, from a lung infection (*Pseudomonas aeruginosa*) that established itself because of his seriously weakened natural defences. The heart itself was reported by Barnard to have maintained an adequate circulation to within five minutes of death;

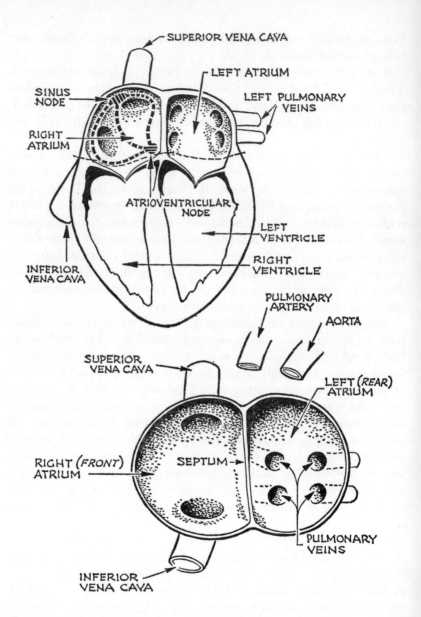

FIG. 25. Sketches showing how the South African (and most subsequent) heart transplants were performed. Recipients retained the upper portion of their own organ (above dotted line in upper sketch) which left intact the natural pacemaker, the sinus or S-A node

174

although this is not at all surprising, for heart muscle as we saw earlier is a remarkably robust material. Even a heart totally severed from the body but kept supplied with fresh blood will continue to beat for some hours, until its supply of essential nutrients runs low.

What emerged from the drama was, first, that in purely mechanical terms the transplantation was entirely successful. The delicate plumbing, carried out under conditions that were probably nearly ideal for the 'state of the art', was most skilfully executed—as witness the patient's astonishingly speedy recovery from the surgery itself. Whether the operation was justifiable at that stage must remain in dispute. But here was an operation that combined unusual emotional appeal with the possibility of an intensely practical application, in that half the deaths in highly developed nations today are the consequence of cardio-vascular diseases. Moreover, one-sixth of the Americans who died of these diseases in 1965 were under sixty-five years of age—people in the prime of life, one might say.

Would the South African achievement stampede other surgeons into performing the operation; surgeons possibly less skilled in a very delicate operation but envious of the prestige, personal or national, that accrued to those willing to attempt it? Barnard and a number of other surgeons in the U.S.A., Britain, France, Russia and elsewhere had already perfected their surgical technique in a long series of successful transplantations between dogs, an animal in which the mechanics of heart surgery is even more difficult than in humans.

In fact, a second heart transplantation was attempted only three days after the first, when a nineteen-day-old 'blue baby' in Maimonides Hospital in New York received the heart of another baby, although it lived only another seven hours. But there was another factor involved here: the immunological defences were thought to have been sufficiently immature in the recipient to permit success, had its clinical condition been better.

Within a year of the world's first human-to-human heart transplantation a hundred attempts had been made by more than a dozen surgical teams in five different continents. Most of the recipients died within a few days, although one, Dr Philip Blaiberg, was still alive at the time of writing, fourteen months

175

after his operation, sustained on substantially the same immuno-suppressive regime prescribed by Professor Barnard for his first heart transplant patient. Some of the recipients were nursed on an immuno-suppressive regime that included the new drug A.L.S., along with azathioprine and small doses of steroids.

But the criterion of success for a kidney transplant is one year's survival. There are indications that the public is growing dis-illusioned by the high mortality rate, and with the fact that heart patients who may (or may not) have passed peacefully away as their heart gave up the struggle are now dying in circumstances of considerable distress, as a result of an overwhelming infection.

But these are early days yet for a new and ambitious surgical technique, and as with kidney grafts much will depend on the skills of individual surgeons. One American surgeon, Dr Denton Codey of St Luke's Episcopal Hospital in Houston, has already established a high rate of success. A Register of Human Heart Transplants analogous to the kidney register in Boston was set up at Groote Schuur Hospital in Cape Town in 1968.

LUNG TRANSPLANTATION

The lung, like the kidney, is a paired organ, and amenable to surgical technique, but otherwise its transplantation suffers from the same four basic technical problems as the heart. A lung trans-plant from one man to another was first undertaken in 1963, when a convict serving a life sentence and seriously ill from three different diseases received a lung from the victim of a heart attack, in an operation performed by Dr James Hardy at the University of Mississippi Medical Center. The man lived for eighteen days with his newly acquired organ functioning for the whole period, only to die of kidney disease. As is often the case with kidneys, the lung had been preserved in transition between donor and recipient by keeping it cool and perfusing with oxygen and a solution of the anticoagulant heparin.

So far, however, homografted lung tissue has proved a great disappointment. No matter how healthy the original lung, nor how carefully the organ is preserved, the tissue gradually dies after implantation. The trouble seems to lie with an attack that takes place right at the interface with the pulmonary blood supply. At the time of writing, optimism runs higher for an artificial organ based on the new silicone membrane structures; although such a prosthesis may be some years away yet.

At least one attempt has been made to transplant the heart and lungs as a one-piece sub-assembly. There are some compelling reasons for replacing the entire contents of the chest, among them the fact that the trio grows up together and functions in concert, while the 'plumbing' is simpler, only two reconnections of blood vessels, compared with nine for a solo heart transplant. It is also believed that the excision of a lung may interrupt the supply of some essential secretion but that this can be avoided by transferring the three-organ structure intact.[11] As with the heart graft the crown of the heart including the right atrium and natural pacemaker is retained, while the entire pulmonary circulation is left intact.

LIVER TRANSPLANTATION

1963 also saw the first attempts to transplant a liver, the heaviest and bloodiest organ, weighing about three pounds in a full-grown man, and much the most difficult organ to transfer. They were made by Dr Thomas Starzl of the University of Colorado School of Medicine in Denver. He used cadaver livers, in an operation that involves many reconnections, some of which are obscured by the size of the organ. All four of his patients died that year, but his more recent attempts have proved longer-lived.

But transplants of livers in animals — pigs and dogs mostly — have been far more successful, and have led research workers to the idea that the liver may be an 'immunologically favoured' organ, less susceptible to a rejection response. On the other hand, it is well known that azathioprine, the immuno-suppressive drug that has found most favour in kidney transplantation, is in fact damaging to the liver. Dr Starzl has concentrated on the development of a regime based on A.L.S.

Meanwhile, a Bristol team under Mr Joseph Peacock, whose pig Percy had by October 1967 survived fifteen months with another pig's liver inside him, has focused its efforts on methods for preserving a liver in perfect condition. They believe it will be necessary to store a liver for at least six hours to give the surgeons time to transplant without cell damage.

There are times when an organ either ceases to function or

requires a rest, given which there is a chance it will regain its former proficiency. The artificial kidney was originally developed for this purpose, and there are devices today that can temporarily relieve the heart of some of its workload. No such man-made system exists in the case of the liver, however; nor is one likely until we know far more about the mechanism of this complex bio-chemical 'factory'. But there remains the possibility of using a natural liver in a temporary capacity.

In October 1966, Mrs Cynthia McPhail gave birth prematurely to a stillborn baby in an Australian hospital, following which both her liver and kidneys failed and her blood became infected. She was admitted, unconscious, to the Alfred Hospital in Melbourne, where it was decided to try a technique which was then still under development in the U.S.A. and Britain. This was to bypass her blood through the liver of a pig. The liver from a pig weighing about 40 kilograms was excised and washed free from its blood, then joined by cannulae to an artery and vein in the patient's arm. The blood flowed through the liver into a reservoir, from whence it was pumped back into her arm.

After nine hours of this treatment the girl's blood was considerably improved. Two days later it was repeated for another eight hours, and the girl began to regain consciousness. For a further two weeks she was treated with an artificial kidney and with antibiotics, whereupon both liver and kidneys regained their normal function. She left hospital after six weeks to resume a normal life.

The same organ, cleansed each time, can be used to treat more than one patient. The technique, when perfected, is likely to be employed to sustain the recipient of a transplanted liver through the first hours or days after a transplantation, until the liver regains its full function.

The Groote Schuur team in Cape Town took the technique a stage further when they used a live baboon to provide temporary liver function for a young woman dying of liver disease. They replaced the baboon's blood with human blood of a group compatible with the patient, then arranged for her blood to flow through the anaesthetized animal. Within seventy-two hours of the commencement of cross-circulation, her surgeon reported that the woman was 'lucid, orientated and fully conscious'.[12] After seven days of assistance from the sleeping baboon she made a dramatic recovery, her own liver regaining its function.

In Britain, where 200 to 300 people under fifty die each year from such diseases as cirrhosis and cancer of the liver, the first liver transplantations were carried out in 1968. Of the five transplants carried out by Professor Roy Calne of Cambridge and Dr Roger Williams, consultant physician at King's College Hospital in London, three regained the use of a healthy liver. One woman of forty-six lived for eleven weeks with the liver of a five-year-old child; and a man of forty-one even returned to work only six weeks after the operation, with the liver of a thirteen-year-old child, although he too has since died. These operations, the surgeons reported, afforded 'considerable hope' that liver transplants would have much to offer patients with fatal liver disease or damage. When perfected, they foresaw the operation offered to perhaps 130 to 160 people in Britain each year.[13]

If anything, the liver is even more susceptible than other organs to damage after death. The liver, the British surgeons conclude, must be cooled within fifteen minutes of death if the transplanted organ is to regain its function. Simple cooling to 4°C is enough to prevent deterioration for two or three hours, but beyond that some form of continuous perfusion is needed. Even so, the liver has been preserved in good shape for only about eight hours.

Nor is there an artificial version of this complex bio-chemical 'factory' with which the surgeon might restore the health of a dying patient before operating, or tide him over any delay in the grafted organ regaining its function or any attempt at rejection. The best prospect, as we have seen, is to use an animal's organ in a temporary capacity.

OTHER ORGANS

Another organ was transplanted successfully for the first time in 1967, by two professors with the University of Minnesota, Richard C. Lillehei and William Kelly. Their patient was a woman of thirty-two, diabetic since childhood, who on New Year's Eve was provided with a cadaver pancreas implanted in the left-hand side of her abdomen and a cadaver kidney implanted on the right side. She regained both a secretion of insulin and her renal function. The pancreas was transplanted in its entirety, along with some ten inches of duodenum; the donor being a woman of thirty-seven who had died in a respirator.

Four months later the same team operated on another woman, of forty-six and in good health until stricken by an intestinal trouble that they found to be caused by a blocking of the blood supply to the entire bowel. They took the decision to attempt a transplantation of a whole bowel, large and small, from a teenage boy who was dying of cerebral haemorrhage. When the boy died the cadaver was kept on a heart-lung machine to maintain the bowel in prime condition until the operating team had prepared the recipient. But this time the patient died, twelve hours after the operation—a consequence, Dr Lillehei believed, of extensive blood clotting.

Transplantation of the spleen has also been attempted, in the belief that a fresh spleen would supply a haemophiliac with the missing agent that allowed him to bleed so freely. But some have expressed doubt whether this operation, even if successful, would compensate for the disadvantages of turning a haemophiliac into an 'immunological cripple'.

The transplantation of a complete joint such as a knee is one target of the team led by Professor David Slome at the Royal College of Surgeons in London. The aim is the transfer of an entire working unit of bone, cartilage and blood vessels, using an immuno-suppressive regime based on A.L.S. But the research team, although successful with animals, is conscious that the drawbacks of the regime and the technical difficulties of rejoining all the vessels involved at present outweigh prospective advantages to a person suffering, for example, from arthritis. An artificial joint is likely to remain much easier to install. But there is also the prospect of replacing the cartilage lining of an arthritic joint with healthy cartilage from a freshly amputated limb. Cartilage, like the cornea, is not nourished by the blood itself, and evokes no immunological response. It is widely used by the plastic surgeon.

Beyond lies the possibility of grafting an even more complex sub-assembly such as a whole limb. This may well be simpler than the transplantation of a joint because the blood vessels are so much larger.

In 1962 surgeons in Boston rejoined the right arm of twelve-year-old Everett Knowles after a railway accident had completely amputated it just below the shoulder. No one yet knows to what extent function and feeling will be restored but reconstructive surgery has undoubtedly restored the fractured humerus and the ruptured blood supply. Chinese and British surgeons more recently have claimed similar successes following factory accidents, although always the original limb has fortuitously been found. So in each case the graft was an autograft, and no immunological response was invoked.

Many medical men believe that the spinal cord, once severed, cannot be repaired, and the paralysis must therefore be overcome by other means. But in 1966 Professor Leslie Freeman, director of the surgical research laboratories at Indiana University Medical Center, announced that a team in his charge had devised means of regenerating nerve connections in severed spines that he believed could lead to complete recovery in certain cases of paraplegia.

One of his earlier discoveries was that nerve cells continue to grow in the area around a spinal injury, and he believed the growth might be sufficient to repair an injury. Normally, however, scar tissue impenetrable to the growing nerves soon fills the fracture. Then a Formosan scientist at the Center, Dr Chun Ching Kao, had the idea that a bridge might be built for the nascent nerve cells by auto-grafting nerve cells from the victim's brain. (They could be removed without ill-effect from the periphery of the brain.)

In the first experiments with animals the brain tissue soon died, and scar tissue developed before the spinal nerves rejoined. But a second member of the team, Dr Shimu Yoshifusa, found a way of culturing the slivers of brain tissue before using it to repair the breach. They reported that many of their animals had recovered completely within four months.

One of the risks, however, of trying this technique on a human being is that the nerves will reconnect in a disconcerting manner. In dogs it does not much matter how this happens for they still seem to recover the use of their hindquarters. But humans, thinks Dr Freeman, may be upset by a strange new system of nerve connections, and would need physical therapy and psychiatric help to recover from the operation. He also admits difficulty in culturing neuronal tissue in the quantities needed.

In 1908 Charles Guthrie, an American vascular surgeon,

performed a homograft of a complete sub-assembly, a dog's head. He grafted an extra head on to a dog, so creating briefly a two-headed Cerberus, both heads of which showed every sign of being awake and alert. The reflex and voluntary movement of the grafted head were reported to be 'good'. Russian surgeons led by Professor Anatoli Kanevsky have recently repeated the experiment, and report that their twin-headed dogs usually survive for seven to nine days. 'During this period the animal eats, sleeps and performs its physiological functions normally as if nothing had happened,' Professor Kanevsky told a conference in Milan in 1968, adding improbably that 'having two heads and two mouths it eats twice as much'.

Although we still do not understand the underlying mechanism involved in immunological rejection, it is plain that the more closely related are the donor and recipient, the greater the chance of a successful union. By the same token it would appear that the surgeon is asking for a little too much in attempting the xenograft, the transplanting of tissues from another species altogether. Yet there is the astonishing case of a chimpanzee's kidney that survived for nine months in a girl. The young woman, a school teacher of twenty-three, was given the ape's organ in a transplant operation performed by Dr Keith Reemtsma in New Orleans in 1964. She was given doses of azathioprine and prednisone daily until she succumbed to the 'complications of immune suppression'.

In their medical report Dr Reemtsma, now professor of surgery at the University of Utah School of Medicine, and his team discuss six patients dying of kidney disease in whom they transplanted the kidneys of apes.[14] These operations were performed between November 1963 and February 1964, and the longest to live was the schoolteacher.

In the discussion that followed this paper one surgeon raised a disconcerting complication he had encountered with the xenograft. The task it performs for its own species may be slightly yet significantly different from that required by *homo sapiens*. He had transplanted both kidneys from a 130-pound chimpanzee into a man. They functioned only too well, execreting fluids so rapidly that within hours the man was dehydrated—literally drained of body fluids. Next morning he suffered a stroke and he died of a coronary three days later. The trouble, thought the surgeon, was that the chimpanzee's kidneys have evolved to handle a diet much richer in potassium than our own.

Some of the attractions of the xenograft are fairly obvious, among them the comparatively ready availability of 'spare parts' and the fact that they could be kept 'on the hoof' until needed. Different animals are potential sources of different components. The pig, for example, already 'cannibalized' for its skin, also supplies heart valves, as many as three of which have been transplanted into one human heart. Unsuccessful attempts have also been made to transplant its heart and liver. The baboon, already shown to be highly tolerant of human blood, is another possibility ; or a greyhound, whose heart has a capacity roughly equal to that of a man, might be the source of a new heart in the peak of condition.

But the key to the xenograft lies with an immuno-suppressant more potent yet more selective than those used today.

BIOLOGICAL ENGINEERING

Today roughly a third of all surgery is performed for the excision of cancers. But surgical practice is about to undergo fundamental changes with, on the one hand, the rapid growth in importance of restorative surgery of all kinds, and on the other, if perhaps a few years away yet, the prospect that immunological investigations will yield ways of suppressing the growth of malignant tissue. But there remains a technical matter of considerable importance — socially, ethically, even psychologically. This is the source of living tissues with which repairs and renovations might be made.

Where, for example, might the U.S.A. find up to 50,000 kidneys a year — the total number of Americans that die of kidney disease ; or up to 400,000 new hearts — one estimate of the market potential? Any expectation that heart transplants would soon be available for those suffering from advanced heart disease was unrealistic, concluded the Planning Unit of the British Medical Association, in a report early in 1969. 'It seems unlikely that heart transplantation can make a serious contribution to the general problem of degenerative heart disease.' Its real value, the report concluded, was more likely to lie in congenital heart disease in infants.

Even corneas must be removed from the eyes within eight hours of death and cooled to 4°C, otherwise putrefaction sets in. In

183

Britain the Human Tissue Act of 1961 requires that corneas (or any other part of the cadaver) may be excised only by a fully registered medical practitioner. It limits the source in practice virtually to those hospitals where reliance can be placed on the medical staff to summon doctors from the eye bank in time to obtain the necessary permission from relatives, and then to remove the eyes before they deteriorate. This appears to be the major obstacle at present to a larger supply of eyes: an obstacle that might be removed completely if public opinion were to permit the collection of corneas by skilled technicians—a task well within their capacity, although obviously fraught with ethical hazards.

Then again, fresh corneas must be implanted within about forty-eight hours, which places a further restriction on the surgeon's freedom. Corneas can be preserved by deep freezing in liquid nitrogen, but this complicates the procedure for the surgeon, and so far only half-thickness grafts have been consistently successful. The deeper cells of the cornea are vulnerable to freezing and have very little power of regeneration. Half-thickness grafts that stop short of the vulnerable layers have been made successfully, but only very recently have full-thickness grafts of frozen tissue proved possible, using corneas whose cells had been protected by an 'anti-freeze' compound.

STORING LIVING TISSUE

Normally, those tissues that serve merely to provide stroma, a temporary scaffold around which new tissue might grow, are stored in a refrigerator at temperatures as low as $-80°C$. They include skin, bone, blood and blood vessels, even heart valves (see Plates 35 and 36) but to store an 'active' item such as a kidney or a whole heart it seems likely that a machine akin to a heart-lung machine will be required, to keep the organ perfused with undamaged and freshly oxygenated blood.

Such a machine is undergoing clinical trials in Britain (see Plate 37). It has been developed in Vickers Research Laboratories at Ascot, the outcome of earlier work on the efficacy of oxygen under pressure for the restoration of tissues dying of frostbite or gas gangrene, for example. The Vickers team under Dr Ian Hopkinson collaborated over much of this period with Dr John

Ackermann, a South African surgeon whose early work was with Professor Barnard.

The hyperbaric perfusion unit, as the organ store is called, can be likened to a test-bed on which the 'bio-mechanism' is kept running. The organ is coupled to a supply of freshly oxygenated human blood, although the rate of perfusion is much lower than nature provides. At the same time two conditions are applied that slow the metabolic processes—which include those of death and putrefaction. They are to expose the organ to oxygen under pressure, and to cool it to 5 °C.

The organ sits in a cradle and, once connections have been made to its blood vessels, is lowered into the transparent pressure vessel atop the unit (see Fig. 26). It is wholly submerged in the cold perfusate—half blood and half other chemicals—in an atmosphere

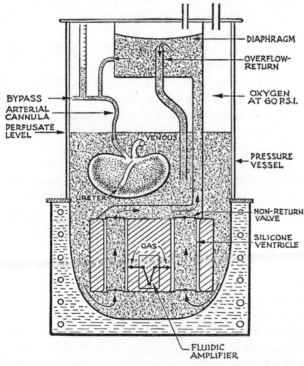

FIG. 26. Vickers's system for storing an organ under high-pressure oxygen, at low temperature and continuously perfused with blood

of oxygen at sixty pounds per square inch. A 'gentle' pump regulated by a fluidic switch circulates perfusate slowly through the organ.

The present machine is a sophisticated piece of apparatus, but it should be possible to simplify the control if straightforward storage is all that is needed. In the case of the kidney, there is hope that the organ's condition might readily be assessed merely by measuring the glucose content of the urine it discharges. Glucose is easy to estimate.

But there is every prospect that machines of this type will prove satisfactory for storing other organs, hearts especially, once optimum conditions have been found for perfusion.

Much smaller machines are also taking shape, perhaps small enough to fit into a suitcase, which could be rushed to the scene of an accident, to accept an organ from a donor immediately following his death. They will use a semi-permeable silicone membrane in the oxygenator, of the kind discussed in the last chapter in connection with artificial lungs.

Should it ever prove possible to make extensive use of animal tissues in human repairs, it may be more satisfactory to preserve the tissue in the living animal until required. Barnard has even suggested that live baboons whose blood had been replaced with human blood might be used as a temporary repository for human hearts. His colleagues had previously shown that the baboon can tolerate a complete transfusion with human blood (see also p. 178).

Pigskin is an excellent example of a tissue that is banked in this way. It is used by the King's County Hospital, Brooklyn, to dress large raw areas of flesh, as with the more serious burns (and in one case for the treatment of a premature baby born without skin on some of its limbs). In this case the 'bank' consists of young pigs, just weaned, husbanded for the purpose by the hospital.

When skin is required the pig is first shaved, scrubbed with antiseptic soap, and washed with alcohol. Sheets of split-thickness skin are then removed with an electric dermatome and immersed in a saline solution containing penicillin. So treated, the skin is laid over the flayed areas, to which it adheres in a matter of hours. More than one such dressing may be needed before the patient's own skin has begun to regenerate; or in other cases the pigskin may be applied merely as a temporary expedient while an autograft is being prepared.

'The pig is a greatly under-appreciated animal,' wrote Leo K. Bustad, a Californian professor with a lifelong interest in the animal.[15] 'In anatomy and physiology the pig is remarkably like a man. Its heart and circulatory system, its diet, its alimentary tract and even its teeth are very similar to those of a human being ... I have never ceased to be amazed at how much pigs resemble people.' With a long history as an experimental animal dating back to Leonardo da Vinci, very recently as a midget pig at a weight little more than the average for man, this undervalued creature may yet emerge as man's best friend in the most intimate of senses.

One advantage of a non-human source of 'spare parts' is that intensive inbreeding might well be used to produce genetically homogeneous tissue that should help further to overcome the immunological barrier to its acceptance. Another, perhaps greater advantage is that it will avoid some of the grave moral and ethical conflicts that could easily arise should — as now seems possible — we solve some of the bio-chemical and technical problems of transplantation before we can reach what Lederberg has called 'a moral consensus on the organization of the market for allocation of precious parts'.[16] Blood is already bought and sold in the U.S.A. Eye banks in Britain, although seriously short of tissue, which when they can spare it they supply free of charge to fellow-surgeons overseas, have been approached by rich Arab states whose *mores* would not permit their own people to donate, with offers to purchase the coveted corneas.

Surgeons who work in this area are generous in their praise of the general public. One, concerned chiefly with kidney transplants, finds his requests for the kidneys of deceased persons are never resented and seldom refused if properly put to the relatives. The number of people who believe they will need both their kidneys in the hereafter is comparatively small. How long will it be, however, before it becomes generally known that kidneys and other living tissues, if harvested promptly enough, have a scarcity value that could be considerable, certainly running to thousands of pounds for an organ. And there have already been cases of a single corpse donating a heart, two kidneys and two corneas.

The problem grows worse if we consider what in the view of some surgeons is potentially the most suitable source of human organs, namely the person who through accident or disease has suffered irreversible brain damage. Very often cerebral cripples are (or become) fully unconscious, and almost inert, although otherwise perfectly healthy. With careful nursing they may be preserved in this state of coma for months, even years—until they succumb to an infection, usually of the lungs. But the surgeon is well aware from measurements of the electrical activity (E.E.G.) of the brain that his patient can never regain consciousness, nor even continue to breathe without the assistance of a respirator.

Inevitably, there comes a point when it is in everyone's interest —patient, relatives and medical staff—to 'turn off the switch'. Normally, this will happen only when the patient contracts a terminal infection such as broncho-pneumonia—which itself is liable to damage certain organs. But once the technical problems of transplantation are resolved, as is already the case with the kidney, the case purely on grounds of logic for regarding the unconscious cerebral cripple as a source of spare parts to be 'cannibalized' may become overwhelming. Moreover, there will inevitably be economic pressures on the relatives, especially where the patient was the breadwinner, to gain compensation from this source.

The exceptional circumstances of the unconscious cerebral cripple afford the surgeons ample time to match tissues with those of potential recipients, and to confirm that the donor's medical history includes nothing that might be inimical to an exchange of tissue. At the same time it allows the surgeon to prepare the recipient, unrushed.

Questions of moral, ethical and spiritual concern have ever accompanied—some would say plagued—medical progress, but at a pace leisurely enough for man to contain them. No longer is this the case, so rapidly has 'spare parts surgery' progressed. Matters which the doctor is often ill-equipped to judge are now being thrust upon him. Nor is this a matter in which we can rely on the laws of economics to arrive at an acceptable solution. Their guidance will do no more than plunge us deep in what a British scientist, Heinz Wolff, calls the 'mathematics of misery'—calculations designed to sift the few who may live from the many who must die prematurely.

188

CHAPTER SIX

Man Modified

'It is clear that the general quality of the world's population is not very high, is beginning to deteriorate, and should and could be improved.'

Sir Julian Huxley, F.R.S.

'Not everybody wants to live with someone else's heart inside him. It's an eerie thing.'

Dr Denton Cooley

THE growing intimacy of interaction between man and foreign mechanisms, whether living or man-made, is exposing fresh problems, no less difficult of solution than the older ones. These are 'people problems', social rather than technical in nature, the concern not just of doctors and surgeons but of the manufacturer and politician, the lawyer and the cleric, even of the accountant. Indeed they are the concern of every one of us, as potentially 'modified men'. Nor can it be said that these are simple matters, easily resolved once the technology is established, for they question some of the fundamental tenets of society as we know it today.

But before we consider these problems, first let us try to put a time scale of the developments discussed and foreshadowed in the previous chapters. 'Crystal gazing' among scientists has been growing into a highly respected and valued management technique in the past few years. The idea is not simply to try to predict the development of technology and society, or to guess when 'breakthroughs' may occur, but to attempt to influence the

189

direction and pace of development instead of just letting things take their course. Dr Erich Jantsch, one of the prophets of this new and potentially immensely valuable cult of 'forecasting the future', writing in an issue of *Science Journal* devoted to the subject,[1] sought to establish its respectability by saying that 'today about 600 large and medium-sized American firms carry out their own technological forecasting on a regular basis, spending around one per cent of their total research and development budget upon it, equivalent to 50 million to 100 million dollars a year.'

There are at least a score of different basic approaches to the technological forecast, but one of the most promising is known as the Delphi model, the development of Dr Olaf Helmer of the RAND Corporation, and described by Jantsch as 'essentially a refinement of the original brainstorming technique'. The difference is that in seeking the views of many experts, which is the essence of brainstorming, special precautions are used by Helmer to make these experts sharpen their own thinking and to prevent them exchanging opinions with one another.

Using a panel of 20 experts in a study conducted at the RAND Corporation, Dr Helmer produced a remarkable table of 'major breakthroughs', and roughly when they could be expected. Part of this table is reproduced in Fig. 27. It makes at least two points that are highly relevant to this book: that the technology we have been discussing is widely believed to be well within grasp, and that in such cases as the transplantation and implantation of organs there is already an urgent need to resolve some of the 'people problems'.

THE COST OF HUMAN ENGINEERING

As an example, let us take what might be called a 'broad spectrum' problem, the question of reliability, which is closely related of course to cost. There is no doubt whatever that living mechanisms have a most remarkable record of reliability. Dr R. Shafer, of General Dynamics' Convair Division, who investigated for the National Heart Institute the application of an Air Force systems management technique to the development of the artificial heart, calculated that the failure rate of the human heart with up to 45 years of continuous service was 3·7 chances in 100 million. Even

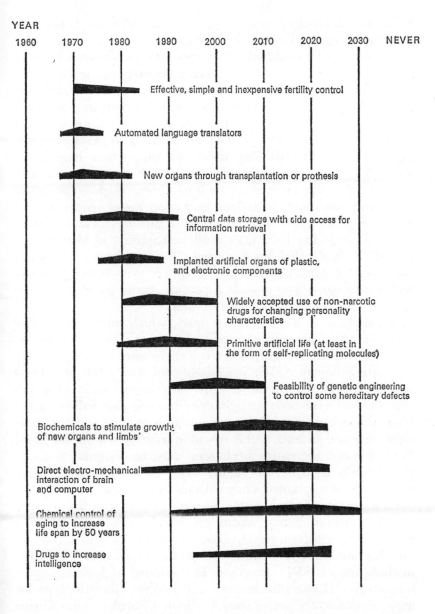

FIG. 27. Forecast of 'breakthroughs' in man-machine relationships, obtained by the Delphi technique of technological forecasting (after *Science Journal*)

for hearts that had given 65 to 75 years of service, the failure rate was still less than 1·6 chances in a million.

The best Shafer could offer for an artificial pump was a figure of 98 per cent reliability over a 10-year period; one, nevertheless, that would be thought exceptionally good by modern engineering standards, considering that an artificial heart once in place must be considered inaccessible for any kind of routine maintenance.

Two pieces of technology that are designed to extraordinarily high standards of reliability today are gas turbine engines for airliners and the electronic repeaters used in trans-oceanic telephone cables. The engines are built to withstand gross excesses of stress and corrosion for as long as 12,000 hours (equivalent to 4 million miles flown by a 707 or DC8 airliner); the repeaters, once the cable has been laid, must be regarded as virtually inaccessible, that is they must survive a life of at least 20 years: in each case at peak performance. Both are very costly pieces of technology, 50 to 100 pounds a pound, chiefly by virtue of the engineering standards expected of them.

An artificial organ such as a heart, which must not for one moment falter, will combine cardinal features of each: 35 million cycles a year in a highly corrosive environment, under widely fluctuating demands, yet inaccessible for any kind of routine maintenance. In addition, it must be designed from materials that will cause the body no irritation, in a way that will cause the blood no serious damage nor encourage it to clot. Some method must be found to anchor this machine securely within the chest. What is more, the entire mechanism must be designed in a way that permits it to be thoroughly sterilized so that no infective organisms are implanted along with the new organ.

Infection is a considerable hazard in orthopaedic surgery, especially where implantations are being introduced into the tissues. One British surgeon has countered the risk with a 'production line' operating technique akin to the 'clean room' assembly methods now widely practised in building high-performance instruments. His technique may well become the prototype for more extensive reconstruction. Dr John Charnley, who directs the Centre for Hip Surgery at the Wrightington Hospital in Lancashire, specializes in replacing the hip joint with one of his own design, of stainless steel and high-density polyethylene. His technique is to enclose his patient in a capsule of air filtered almost free from bacteria (see Plate 38), and perform the operation in stages, each with its own sterilized kit of tools which once used is promptly removed from the scene. Dr Charnley claims in this way to have reduced his infection rate to the remarkably low level of 0·6 per cent.

Another recent development that will go far to assist the designer is the use of gamma-rays instead of heat to sterilize surgical supplies, from syringes to heart valves. 'Bone banks' in Poland and Austria now use radiation to prepare bone for storage in readiness for transplantation. Man-made mechanisms such as hearts could be prepacked in containers and sealed before gamma-sterilization, without the slightest risk of distortion or of residual radioactivity.

Experience with relatively simple implantable systems such as joints and pacemakers has already revealed how infuriating the environment can be. One serious problem is the risk of a violent reaction between living tissues and fine particles of an implanted material like nylon or polytetrafluoroethylene (P.T.F.E.)—tiny fragments worn away in an artificial joint, for example—even though the tissues are unperturbed by the same material in bulk.

Another problem is the difficulty of finding materials that combine an adequate fatigue life (fatigue being responsible for about 90 per cent of all engineering failures) with a resistance to a form of corrosion more savage than that which causes deterioration all around us. This applies even to apparently stationary components like electrical leads, which in fact are constantly being flexed by body motion and flushed by its fluids. The average useful life of a cardiac pacemaker is only about two years—and broken leads and ingress of body fluids are among the most frequent causes of trouble. One British survey, of the pacemakers implanted in the twelve months ending March 1966, found that in 57 per cent of the cases the pacemaker itself had failed in some way.[2]

Small wonder, then, that most large chemical companies, on whom we might expect to rely for the highly specialized materials needed for implantation, have fought shy of pioneering in a field where the ultimate success—and the profits—will surely go to the engineering firms that can comply with an exceptionally rigorous specification. Davies and McCarthy of Imperial Chemical Industries in their book on technological economics go as far as to conclude that 'economics offers no adequate incentive for the socially very important activity of making and designing materials for surgical components such as artificial hearts, artificial joints and large numbers of other materials, including false teeth.'[3] Society, they believe, 'must take steps to have this research done on a different basis'; a conclusion they reach on the basis of investigations made at I.C.I.'s central research laboratories into the prospects medical engineering might afford as a new market for polymers.

But a piece of plastic worth only a few pence when suitably fashioned and sterilized may acquire a market value of pounds, perhaps many pounds. The 'spiral' or intra-uterine method of contraception is a good example here.

One company that has put a major effort into polymers for medical purposes is the Dow Corning Corporation of Midland, Michigan, whose Dow Corning Center for Aid to Medical Research is world-renowned for its Silastic range of silicone rubber materials. Made to medical-grade standards of purity, these resins are among the least toxic, most immutable materials known to man. Even so, surgeons and scientists alike are baffled by curious changes, from discolouration to gross shrinkage, that have taken place in some silicone aortic ball valves after a few years of service.

The responsibility of a manufacturer in a case of failure of an implanted device has still to be settled in law, but quite plainly the vigilance now exercised in the case of pharmaceutical products must be extended to include implantable devices. In the U.S.A. the Food and Drug Administration, whose responsibility this aspect will presumably become, has its own Bill before Congress that will require manufacturers to meet what are generally acknowledged to be very high standards. (The F.D.A., a Swiss drug firm executive once told me rather wryly, requires not just the truth but the whole truth.) It would include, as with drugs, the pre-marketing clearance of the prosthesis. One estimate puts the cost of testing a new polymer for implants to F.D.A. requirements at several million dollars over five years. In Britain the final responsibility is likely to rest with the Dunlop Committee, at present concerned with the safety of drugs.

194

In Czechoslovakia surgeons are going as far as to take one or more of each small batch of heart pacemakers and place them on test under physiological conditions simulated by an analogue computer. This is done at the Czechoslovak Research Institute for Medical Electronics and Modelling in Prague, where the pacemakers kept on test are monitored continuously for the very first signs of impending trouble, whereupon those already in service from the batch would forthwith be replaced.

Plainly the 'Rolls-Royce' approach to engineering the prosthetic market seems to demand will not easily be acquired, and certainly not cheaply.

On the other hand, the needs of the surgeon may prove to be less remote from other needs than seems the case at present. Take the heart, for example, one feature of which is an ability to pump a very easily damaged fluid without destroying cells more rapidly than the body can replace them. But industry sometimes makes and uses very sensitive fluids — nitroglycerine, for example — that need to be handled by a 'gentle' pump, which helps to stimulate its interest. The process of molecular filtration used in the artificial kidney is beginning to look economically attractive for the purification of contaminated water. Radio pills are no less useful for following the progress of food through a canning factory than food through the gut.

Many of the most exciting and most valuable advances in the field of man-machine interactions have come about through a symbiosis of intellectual disciplines, between surgeon and engineer, mathematician and psychologist, chemist and physiologist; or through more complex permutations. A toolmaker once told me how he saved the leg of a patient who was with him in hospital, by explaining to the surgeons how they might extract the badly corroded screws of an earlier bone implant. Once surgeon, engineer and scientist learn to talk freely to one another, progress can be astonishingly rapid — witness many of the mechanisms, from shunts to hearts, discussed in this book.

THE HUMAN FACTOR

One factor which is easily overlooked in the excitement of surmounting the formidable technical problems of the machine itself is the cosmetic factor in matching man and machine. Yet this human factor if neglected can invalidate excellent work on the prosthesis. The engineering must be tailored to the patient, physically, aesthetically and psychologically. A serious distortion of the body's shape or of the motions whereby it makes a manoeuvre may appear to others little short of grotesque, in which case the wearer may well prefer to make do with what natural functions he still retains.

It may be excellent from an engineering standpoint to have an artificial leg with a knee joint that telescopes instead of bending, or to provide an artificial arm of exceptional reach that works on the 'lazy tongs' principle, but the wearer would undoubtedly find his prosthesis an embarrassment in public. Again, an artificial eye that made random movements would be far more grotesque than one that stared fixedly ahead. There can surely be no more damning indictment of the failure of the engineer than to meet an armless child who prefers to use his toes, to eat for example, rather than the jerky artificial arms he has been given.

Early in October 1967 a young physicist, consultant to a group of London hospitals, approached me with a problem. A few days earlier he had witnessed the implanting of the first of a new kind of bladder pacemaker: a radio-frequency device, the transmitter for which remained outside the patient, leaving only a small coil to be buried sub-cutaneously in the abdomen, coupled by platinum wires to electrodes embedded in the lazy sphincter muscle. A matching coil placed over the buried 'aerial' would then beam a train of tiny electrical pulses to keep the muscle in tone, and the urethra from leaking whenever, for example, a cough or a laugh caused abdominal pressures to rise and compress the bladder. In this way an incontinent person could regain control of the muscle. Several dozen patients, most of them elderly, had already been equipped in this way by the surgeon responsible for its development, Mr K. P. S. Caldwell, of the Royal Devon and Exeter Hospital, using pacemakers made up in his hospital.

But the operation in London involved no elderly incontinent but a young married woman of thirty-one whose troubles had grown steadily worse over four years following her second pregnancy. She had looked forward eagerly to the relief the pacemaker promised from a vexing and humiliating condition that had kept her virtually confined to her home. This woman had been promised the first of a batch of fifty pacemakers manufactured to Mr Caldwell's design for the National Health Service. What neither she nor her surgeon had anticipated was the size and weight of the transmitter she was expected to wear constantly on her tummy. It was the size and shape of a tablet of soap, and no provision whatever had been made to attach it. Could I, the physicist wanted to know, suggest someone who might undertake an urgent job of miniaturizing the transmitter to a cosmetically more acceptable shape and size, and invent a more acceptable means of attachment than sticking plaster?

The story well illustrates the enormous gulf that remains to be bridged between the enthusiastic innovator on the one hand and the patient on the other, before 'human engineering' is likely to be accepted. Any woman could have told those concerned with this pacemaker that it simply was not good enough, however great the relief it might bring. The initial result of 'man-machine inter-action' in this case was the patient's consternation and disappoint-ment at the thought of having undergone an operation only to find herself restricted effectively to wearing loose, maternity-type clothes.

In the event, this story had a happy ending, for a leading British electronics manufacturer undertook the task of redesigning the pacemaker to produce a package only a fraction the size and weight of the original model, slim enough to fit unobtrusively in a pocket in a girdle, for example. It led subsequently to the idea of an 'active' pessary that a woman might wear, that would avoid the need for implanted electrodes.

Another human factor the designer may easily overlook is the need to reassure the patient that all is well with his prosthesis, whenever he is placing great trust in its performance. The 'tails' on some of the intra-uterine contraceptive devices and the tick of some heart pacemakers (see Plate 39), neither of which contribute to the performance, are examples of provisions for the human factor. But quite sophisticated sensors may be required to give adequate warning of impending trouble.

LIVING WITH MACHINES

Man's dependence upon machines of one kind or another is already much greater than most of us appreciate, or wish to acknowledge. When first I began to plan this book I was eager to explore the difficulties of accustoming man, supposedly free and self-determining, to an existence permanently dependent upon a machine. As those explorations progressed I came to realize that for a great many people, perhaps the vast majority in the 'developed' countries, there are no fundamental difficulties, and certainly no insuperable ones, to acceptance of the machine—in principle at least. Man may fulminate against his own dependency, but the inconsistency of his arguments is usually only too readily apparent, as was the case when a well-known Oxford don in a national newspaper article said that the introduction in Britain of breath tests for drivers was 'enslaving men to a machine'. After all, did not Le Corbusier once say that a house was 'a machine to live in'?

In 1968 the motor industries of the world turned out about 17 million prosthetic aids to perambulation. There are nearly 80 million cars registered in the U.S.A., roughly one for every two and a half people—of all ages. The joke in which a young child's parents are asked: 'Can he walk yet?' to receive the reply: 'Yes, but he doesn't need to' is already a social comment. Nor plainly need one be too concerned about complexity, always provided the prosthesis affords sufficient advantage to its wearer. Car driving is no easy skill for many people to acquire, and many in fact never achieve any real measure of proficiency. The World Health Organization attributes nearly four-fifths of all road accidents to the 'human factor'. But so closely can a car become associated with the person—and personality—of its owner that, in the case of the male, any criticism of his driving performance is likely to be received as a reflection upon his masculinity.

The predominant reason for this almost universal acceptance of the car is of course the considerable amplification it affords of man's natural powers: up to ten times the horsepower, giving three to five times man's top speed, and sustained moreover not for the length of a football pitch but for hundreds of miles. But it also provides man with the opportunity for presenting an entirely new front to the world, that need enjoy only minimal relationship with the personality within; in short, it has a cosmetic function.

The image so projected is not necessarily to be seen in the flattering light of motor car advertising, however. In a paper to

198

the National Road Safety Congress in 1967 a British psychologist, Professor John Cohen, of Manchester, remarked that what were normally called 'road accidents' were normally failures of the control system: the control system in the man-vehicle relationship within the traffic system. But many, perhaps most, drivers, he contended, were to a large extent controlled by their vehicles. When a motorist sat at the wheel he became 'a bio-robot, a living mechanism. I like to think of him as a centaur, part man part mechanism.' At one extreme some motorists, he thought, might retain substantial control over themselves and their vehicle, but at the other was a monstrous type of bio-robot whose identity had temporarily been obliterated.

Surely the most subtle irony of all lies in the view, already freely voiced by transplant surgeons even before heart transplantation began in earnest, that the most suitable and prolific source of 'spare parts' should arise as a consequence of this mismatch between man and machine: the young victims of motor accidents, especially those who die from brain damage. One London surgeon has suggested that we should organize collection points at the ends of the motorways to harvest this valuable crop of 'bio-mechanisms'.

The dependency of man on machine already extends far beyond the car. A considerable number of people appear to function more smoothly when their mental processes are lubricated—sedated—with a continuous background of music. I once visited a factory where women were performing delicate grinding operations on wine glasses amid the most fearful din from the ageing machines, to the accompaniment of an unceasing flow of light music. The manager assured me that in the absence of the (almost unrecognizable) music the incidence of cut fingers rose alarmingly.* Ordinary spectacles provide us with another commonplace example; and here the dependence may manifest itself in a slightly disconcerting way, as instanced by an answer in court from a famous opera singer, who said that she had forgotten her spectacles and had therefore been unable to *hear* a certain remark. The likely explanation of course is that those whose hearing is deteriorating tend to compensate, probably unconsciously, by lip-reading.

It has been suggested that before man will accept a machine in

* It has recently been shown that music can maintain and improve the alertness of a person performing a monotonous task.

a role in which instinctively he places a great deal of trust—
piloting an aircraft or driving an express train for example—the
machine must be shown to possess the 'will' to survive. Yet the
psychological block that normally persuades man against all—or
almost all—the evidence to place more faith in another man than
in a machine seems unlikely to hamper the acceptance of a
machine by a man who has no alternative. If it is literally a matter
of life and death, man if *compos mentis* will almost always grasp at
the most slender straw. Of course, the strains of the mismatch may
eventually prove too powerful for the psychology of the individual,
who may decide later than he cannot accept in perpetuity the
intrusion of the machine. One of the (many) factors taken into
account by those who apportion scarce medical facilities such as
artificial kidneys is whether the patient is a sufficiently stable
personality to learn to live with the intrusion. But there were
some even so who discovered how easy it was to opt out, just by
severing the implanted shunt.

Just how much mutilation man himself may be prepared to
undergo in the hope of regaining his health is indicated by an
operation developed very recently in the U.S.A. It is called hemi-
corporectomy, and literally cuts the patient in half, discarding
everything below the rim of the pelvis—legs, rectum, genitalia, and
so on. It was offered to several patients in a New York hospital as
the only alternative to a painful death from abdominal cancer.
Among those who decided that half a life was better than none was
James Cavorti, a forty-nine-year-old clothes presser who, only ten
months after the most mutilating and demoralizing operation
known to surgical science, returned home with a complete lower-
body prosthesis to support his sixty-pound torso.[4]

But stresses can be raised in an unexpected quarter, as Israeli
psychiatrists discovered when they investigated the team administering an artificial kidney unit in a Jerusalem hospital. Both
doctors and nurses, they found, suffered emotional strains. One
reason in the case of the doctors was the conflict between their
feelings of omnipotence, having given life to people who otherwise
would long have been dead, and of anxiety about having the skills
and the necessary objectivity in selecting patients their job
required. The nurses, on the other hand, tended to be over-
protective towards their patients—to over-feed them, for example.[5]

In concluding his contribution on organ transplantation to the C.I.B.A. Symposium on 'Ethics in medical progress' in London in 1966, Dr Joseph Murray remarked that 'the practical possibilities are limitless: progress is so rapid, the need is so great and interest so high that it would be rash to put any limits to future progress in organ transplantation.' He then went still further: 'It is conceivable that for the needs of space travel, completely unanticipated physiological requirements may be met by the grafting of accessory organs, such as extra adrenal glands to overcome the stress of the environment on the Moon, accessory lungs to accommodate the atmospheric conditions on Venus,* or accessory extremities with which to crawl around Jupiter.'

Two scientists with the Rockland State Hospital in Orangeburg, New York, have taken the matter much further. Dr Nathan S. Kline, research director, and Dr Manfred Clynes, chief research scientist, in a paper entitled 'Drugs, space and cybernetics: Evolution to Cyborgs',[6] recognize the ultimate futility of man's attempts to adapt to an environment as totally alien as space simply by trying to encapsulate himself in a tiny bubble of artificial atmosphere. 'The bubble', as they put it, 'all too easily bursts.' Their approach would be to equip man with exogeneous components that would extend the self-regulating functions of the body far enough to adapt to a fresh environment. For such a control system, operating entirely unconsciously, Clynes has coined the term 'Cyborg'.

The Cyborg concept is built around an artificial gland capable of administering very small amounts of chemicals at a controllable rate. The scientists chose the osmotic pressure pump capsule devised by Rose (see p. 149) as a device that could be implanted and controlled down to rates of delivery of less than a hundredth of a millilitre of liquid a day. This pump, in combination with sensing and controlling mechanisms, they believed could form a continuous machine-man controlled loop, operating as an adjunct to the body's own controls.

In this way Kline and Clynes visualized the body's automatic adaptation to a whole range of situations and stimuli. Metabolism

* They will take a lot of accommodating: Russian instruments landed on Venus in 1967 measured a temperature that would melt tin!

might be reduced to a very low level for most of a long spaceflight, to minimize its intake and output, and aroused only if a crisis or some scientifically interesting phenomenon should intrude. (Needless to say this would require the discovery of a 'metabolic inhibitor', a type of drug that does not at present exist, but one that surgeons also would find very useful.) Similarly, the intrusion of radiation would stimulate the circulation of an appropriate counter-acting drug. Other drugs would be used to prolong wakefulness when the occasion demanded, to provide erotic or emotional satisfaction, to intercept an incipient psychosis and, should all else fail, to induce a state of unconsciousness.

Now it is easy to dismiss those who would be willing to undergo modifications as radical as these as a lunatic fringe for whom the 'kicks' will outweigh the dangers of this kind of mutilation. But already there are many skin-divers willing to face the hazards of using their lungs as gills, in order to breathe underwater, a prospect so far demonstrated only with mice, rats and dogs, by the Dutch scientist Johannes Kylstra. One diver has allowed a lung to be filled with weak saline, as a preliminary step to trying to breathe water.[7]

A famous New York plastic surgeon has brought the idea even nearer home with his suggestion, in a lecture in 1963, that some future generation may use plastic surgery prophylactically, actually to *prevent* sickness as organs age and their function deteriorates.[8] Dr Blair O. Rogers of the New York University Medical Center proposed that as we reach a certain age it might be time to consider replacing a given organ with a fresh one, before we suffer any consequences of its deteriorating function: a new heart at thirty-five to forty-five, for example, and a new kidney at forty-five to fifty-five. By 1967 a surgeon from Edinburgh was recommending in a lecture to the Royal College of Physicians that the mitral valve of the heart should be replaced as soon as there was strong evidence that the valve was narrowing.

We can already foresee the prospect of inducing and sustaining major physiological and psychological changes by means of pharmaceuticals, while the artificial gland that will administer the prescribed dose unattended, perhaps for years at a stretch, is close at hand. Perhaps the best-known example of a disease that responds with remarkable success to a life-long administration of a chemical is diabetes, where insulin can restore almost a normal expectation of life. There are those who, viewing the problem globally rather than at a personal level, would regard pregnancy as one of the more serious 'diseases' that afflict mankind today, but one that, from a purely bio-chemical standpoint, could be solved simply and cheaply by prophylaxis — through the administration of drugs.

Many other possibilities invite further exploration, such as the chemical pacemaker to keep the heart-beat regular, which if successful would have obvious advantages over the electronic systems implanted today. Another illustration of a long-term treatment involving minute amounts of a chemical is the treatment for hypopituitary dwarfism. Dr M. S. Rabin of Tufts New England Medical Center injects his dwarfs with just two or three grams of a natural hormone — 'human growth hormone' (H.G.H.) — over a period of some five years. In principle, at least, the artificial gland should serve such a long regime far more conveniently.

The rapid advances that pharmacology has been making in psychotropic drugs tempt one to speculate on the possibility of 'permanent' modifications of the personality through their prolonged administration. An unduly excitable, aggressive or unstable personality might become socially more acceptable if kept permanently in a state of mild sedation. The approach should allay at least some of the misgivings of those who repudiate the use of such mutilating — and irreversible — surgical procedures as lobectomy and castration. Again, an indifferent artist or writer may find his work more satisfying — or more saleable — if he is prepared to risk the consequences of performing under the influence of a hallucinogenic drug such as L.S.D. (lysergic acid diethylamide or 'acid'). Or man, ludicrously vulnerable to radiation, may yet find his atomic indiscretions render it imperative that he boost his own resistance with chemicals in order to survive. It may even prove necessary to provide such a facility for a person equipped with an isotopic-powered organ, with a 'drip feed' of a radiation-suppressing chemical, just as we must expect to provide, in perpetuity, the transplant recipient with immuno-suppressive and anti-inflammatory drugs, or the recipient of an artificial heart with an anti-clotting compound like heparin.

But some of the consequences of protracted exposure to a therapeutic chemical, particularly one alien to the body, are already recognized, and indeed no stage in the evolution of a new drug gets more attention today than toxicological testing. For the group shown in Plate 40 who have received cadaver kidneys, the moon-face that develops through long-term treatment with the counter-inflammatory agent prednisone as part of the immuno-suppressive regime is probably a small price to pay for the restoration of their renal function (although there are, as we have seen, more serious consequences to long-term therapy with steroids). Prostigmine's propensity for amplifying the residual muscle action of the paralysed may far outweigh any side-effects found in its use over the lifetime of the patient. More serious, however, is the newly recognized syndrome of 'transplant lung', a complication of some kidney transplants in which recipients' lungs are seriously damaged.[9] It could still transpire, some scientists believe, that the technique of immuno-suppression itself, by whatever means, carries with it the risk of having cancer run riot in the recipient.

Neglecting cost, is there any other limit at all to what the partnership of surgeon, chemist and engineer may expect to achieve in conferring immortality? Dr Alex Comfort puts the matter in perspective in his contribution to *Man and His Future*:[10] 'A law of diminishing returns operates in pure palliative life preservation, and at great ages cure of one disorder merely exposes, and sometimes aggravates, another—rather as the replacement of a faulty component in an old radio may restore voltages to their original levels and blow out several other components which can no longer stand them.'

Already there are strong indications that in the enthusiastic rush to explore sources of new organs and glands we may be neglecting two areas of medicine of commensurate value: the deterioration with age of the supporting structure or skeleton, and the rising incidence of mental disease. It makes little sense to put a new pump in a machine whose chassis has become dangerously embrittled or whose moving parts are fast seizing solid, or whose capacity for self-control is now suspect.

MIND IN THRALL

'Thou shalt not kill but need'st not strive officiously to keep alive,' wrote Arthur Hugh Clough in *The Latest Decalogue*, albeit with satirical intent.

This book is concerned with living man and the prospects for amplifying and reconstructing him by some form of engineering — electrical, mechanical, chemical, biological, even genetic. It has not discussed those engineering systems that preserve or restore life when man is technically dead: the heart-lung machine that, for a short period in the operating theatre, can bypass a patient's heart, for example, or the defibrillator that can jolt a heart into concerted action once more. These are not systems man can learn to live with. But the respirator, once called the 'iron lung', is a system with which man may have to live for the rest of his life, should disease or injury interrupt the signals that rhythmically expand and contract the chest. Several scores of people find themselves afflicted in this way in Britain each year.

It is a common mistake for healthy people to assume that the physically handicapped also suffer some mental insufficiency. In his book *Horizontal Man* Paul Bates, who at the age of twenty contracted poliomyelitis so severely that in a few days he changed from an active and healthy army officer to someone who will remain almost totally paralysed for the rest of his life, wrote: 'People say, "Does he eat?" "Does he feel?" "Does he want to get married?" My answers are those of a normal man ... Like anyone else I have the same drives, instincts, fears ... but pushing its way clean through the middle of my life was the steady beat of a pump and the painful presence of a tube in my throat. In order that I should be normal these bits of apparatus had to be put in their place with all the rest.'[11]

Bates even met misapprehension from a quarter he might reasonably have expected to be sympathetic and understanding: a professor from Oxford who had helped to develop the respirator that was keeping him alive.

'Each week he would come in on his rounds and usually he would have a train of people following him. An indifferent "good morning" and then he was off with the patter ... "and you see, gentlemen, one of the advantages of this pump is that should the lungs become blocked like so—" he would extend his hand and with the finger and thumb squeeze the tube together—"the pump does not continue to try to force air into the lungs but for so long as the block continues air is allowed to escape and so on and so on and so on ... " all the time considerable mental and physical discomfort. ... Heaven knows it's hard enough for the patient to fight to keep his own personality sufficiently strong to relegate his pump to the background without the doctor joining in on the side of the pump.'

In fact, once the acute physiological problems such as the fever of polio are over, the paralysed person's reaction time and judgment normally remain unimpaired, although he may be left so badly disabled as to lack any means of self-expression, even through speech. In other words, a perfectly normal and active mind may be imprisoned within a body that is almost totally immobilized.

But no matter how disabled he is physically, the victim almost always retains full use of his eyes and his brain, a pattern-recognition system of enormous versatility which the engineer still finds great difficulty in simulating. Provided some way can be found of linking these faculties with an external system, there is every prospect of restoring his mobility in some degree.

This has already been demonstrated in one form by the system developed around Edward Roszak, described on page 90, that has placed him 'on-line' with a computer that permits him to manipulate cutlery and so feed himself. Although psychologically very satisfying to achieve, the motions involved here are very complicated. A simpler approach but one with important implications has arisen through work that began as a spare-time interest for the National Spinal Injuries Centre at Stoke Mandeville. It aims not merely to provide the totally disabled person with some measure of independence but to equip him for a job.

The P.O.S.M. Research Project takes its name from what it calls 'patient-operated selector mechanisms', described earlier. It began in 1960 with simple electro-mechanical systems, tailored to the needs of an individual patient, that provided him with a means of summoning assistance. This type of system has since permitted many patients to go home who would otherwise need the constant attention available only in a specially monitored hospital ward. Out of this enterprise came more sophisticated systems, of wider application, that give the patient some control over his environment. They permit him to use the telephone, switch on lights or heaters, operate a page-turner or micro-film projector, for example. But the latest systems go still further. By

206

harnessing the tetraplegic to a keyboard they open up the possibility not just of a more comfortable existence but of fruitful mental activity.

If we choose the right occupation, says Mr Reginald Maling, who directs the small team developing 'Possum' systems, there is a very good chance of getting the patient competitive again. He can point to people like David Hyde, a director of Hyde and Webster (Carpets) Limited of Alderley Edge in Cheshire, who though paralysed from the neck down since a game of rugby at the age of fifteen, has demonstrated these systems throughout Europe and in Australia. Paul Bates, the polio victim, also travels widely today, aided by 'Possum' systems, as a salesman for a firm making beds for the disabled.

These two young men, Bates and Hyde, show a lively intelligence, but less enterprising minds can still be given very satisfying tasks to do. There is a growing number of jobs that can be performed through the medium of a keyboard, and to these the Project looks for the rehabilitation of many of its patients. For example, the Post Office is installing new kinds of letter-sorting machinery which, although largely automatic, still requires a sorter at one stage to read the name of the town and punch a key corresponding to the name he recognizes. The new 'cordless' telephone switchboards, where all switching is done by keys or push buttons, is another prospect, while keyboard control systems for machine tools offer a third possibility.

The 'Possum' team has not neglected the problem of transporting the disabled person to and from his place of work. In the summer of 1967 it demonstrated an electric vehicle that could be remotely controlled by a tetraplegic with no other motions than small residual movements in the tips of three fingers and the thumb of one hand. This was, in fact, Paul Bates, who succeeded in persuading the Ministry of Transport to accept the idea of a 'remote-controlled' vehicle, and who subsequently passed his driving test in this way.

The psychological advantage of restoring some mobility and usefulness to a badly disabled person needs no emphasis, but there is a physiological advantage too, in that the small muscular movements that so often escape paralysis are developed and strengthened by use. There is also the possibility of amplifying them further by a muscular stimulant such as prostigmine, perhaps administered continuously.

But there is one invention so powerful that, once the person is fully in communication with it, any physical handicaps may tend to fall by the way.

COMMUNING WITH COMPUTERS

We have already taken a glance at the machine that is revolutionizing scientific, commercial and industrial life in the more highly developed countries of the world. Soon the computer will be a machine from which none of us can hope to escape and still remain part of a sophisticated society. Those who learn first how to work with the computer, to use it to amplify what Huxley called the psycho-metabolism, will see to that. For this man-machine marriage promises—some might say threatens—to become so powerful that the unaided brain will find itself gravely handicapped.

For the present, two technical difficulties are preventing anyone unfamiliar with the working of a computer from communicating freely with the machine. The mechanisms and languages whereby man communicates his needs and obtains his responses are still quite primitive, and a definite impediment to a free interaction. Moreover, since anything but a large and powerful machine is unsatisfactory intellectually, and since very few people can afford these multi-million pound machines, we need some way of sharing the power of a big computer as freely as we now share the power from an electrical generator.

We can illustrate the difficulties to some extent by considering that form of communication the great majority of us find most natural and effective: ordinary speech. We learn, by a complex and highly empirical process that starts in the cradle and may well continue throughout our lives, to recognize and understand the subtleties of the spoken word; nuances of accent and emphasis and cadence, as well as the words themselves and the order in which they are arranged. Recently, after some thirty-six years of training in speech recognition, I found myself embarrassingly at cross-purposes with a Scotsman I was interviewing, whose repeated use of the word 'prophet' I had taken each time to be 'profit'. Even when approached in clear, unambiguous speech the computer time needed to process a speech signal may be ten to one hundred times 'real time'; that is, it may take the computer over a minute to unravel just one second of speech—an expensive business just now, with computer time on the most powerful machines costing about five pounds a minute.

Nevertheless, there is already one method of conversing with the computer in a quite intimate manner, this being by way of the graphic display. This is essentially a cathode ray tube driven by its own 'satellite' computer. It draws numerical data from the main machine, refashions and displays it as a drawing, a graph, an isometric projection. And not just a static picture, for at the touch of a key or a 'light pen' the picture can be set to rotate, so giving the viewer the strongest impression of observing a three-dimensional model.

The display type of output—the prototype of which we met earlier in Sketchpad—is one of the most exciting developments in computer technology. It seems to afford for the first time a glimpse into the 'mind' of the computer. The graphic display is the most dramatic step so far in man-computer symbiosis. But far more sophisticated approaches to what might be called 'real time photography' are taking shape in the laboratory, that will yield a far more informative pictorial display, probably in 3-D colour.

The technology of computer graphics is still at a very early stage, and the machines now available tend to be very expensive, but the technology will develop rapidly, so valuable a link with computing power has it proved already. Throughout the U.S.A. and Europe engineering designers are learning to work with an 'electronic notepad' that can display in a twinkle the consequences of a calculation, a modification, a fleeting idea. The more advanced displays will take the rough sketch traced on the face of the screen and rearrange it into a geometric drawing, with its strengths and its weaknesses brought out.

For the first time, man—any man not just the mathematician—and computer are finding they can interact at the touch of a button, a stylus, even a fingertip. The language—drawings and graphs and symbols—is common to both, and each can now comment promptly on the progress of the other. That is the meaning of 'machine-aided cognition'—Project M.A.C. at the Massachusetts Institute of Technology. Even predictive schemes, in which the computer anticipates the consequences of a course of action and displays the results of its foresight are now taking shape.

Oddly enough, for a nation in which innumeracy is widespread, one of the most popular toys available in Britain since 1967 was founded on complicated mathematics. The Spirograph, invention of a British engineer, is a set of precision gears used to guide a pen in drawing complex patterns from epicyclic curves. The Spirograph will prepare the way for the far more sophisticated possibilities of computer graphics, which in the hands of the scientists have already given us computer-generated movies (even 3-D movies) and cartoons, computer vignettes of scientific events the camera has failed to follow, even computer sketches of nudes.

But the machine, computer or otherwise, that responds to the spoken word will come in time, for the difficulty is not an inherent one but once again the amount of computing power required. Still sooner we may have systems sensitive to touch, even to the approach of the fingers. A more difficult matter is the machine that responds to a visual image or pattern, but here too progress is rapid, and the machine that will match a fingerprint or a cancer cell or a handwritten address with one stored in its memory is now close at hand. Further off, but still not to be discounted, is the machine that will respond directly to thoughts.

But can the computer itself be made to think and to reason? The very suggestion that it might has powerful emotional overtones, for these faculties above all are widely regarded as the prerogative of *homo sapiens*; which of course they are not. The answer must be Yes, a computer can be made to think and to reason, albeit in a very limited way indeed at present. A Scottish scientist, Dr Donald Michie, has compared the performance of present machines, and more particularly the programs that serve them, with those *idiots savants* who perform such phenomenal feats of calculation or memory. The truly remarkable aspect of full human intelligence is the sheer breadth and versatility of its memory and its powers of reasoning. But there are glimmerings of intelligence from machines. A computer called Aldous at the University of Texas has already been programmed to simulate such intimate emotions as anger and fear, and even love. As its inventor points out, however, it is a model of personality, and not the real thing—it doesn't really 'feel frightened' when confronted with a person or another machine.[12]

One important quest today is the computer that learns from its own experience — without question one key aspect of intelligence. Such a man-machine symbiosis — computer plus program plus human guidance — could play games, drive a truly versatile industrial robot, even participate with the scientist in formulating new scientific theories.

Experiments in teaching robots some sense include work at the Massachusetts Institute of Technology, where Professor Marvin Minsky has a machine composed of an 'arm', an 'eye', and a 'brain'. You can take a number of cubes of different sizes and tell this machine to stack them in order with the largest at the bottom — no mean intellectual feat for a machine.

Another is the work of Dr Charles Rosen, who manages the applied physics laboratory at Stanford Research Institute in California. He is making an 'intelligent automaton', a small vehicle controlled in real time by a powerful ditigal computer, whose programs already allow it to draw a map of its own surroundings, read it, and use it to find its way about. Two 'arms', an 'eye' and 'cat's whiskers' act as sensors through which it constructs its own mental image of its surroundings, for display on a TV screen. The scenario that follows shows how far its education had progressed by the summer of 1968:

EXAMPLE OF ROBOT BEHAVIOUR

The following scenario illustrates the present abilities of the robot.

(A man is seated at a teletypewriter in a large room containing the robot vehicle and several wooden objects of various sizes, shapes and colours. He types.)

MAN. Wake up.

(The robot vehicle moves its head jerkily, taking several pictures and range readings. Then its wheels move, and it lines itself up parallel to a wall of the room as the teletype responds.)

ROBOT. Ready.

MAN. Go to (15, 10).

(With occasional pauses and 'head' movements for additional sightings, the vehicle moves towards a spot fifteen feet to the right and ten feet forward from its initial position. Occasionally, it bumps into

an obstacle, backs away, and carefully goes round it. A few feet from its goal it stops, since it 'sees' that a large object occupies the target region. The vehicle travels halfway around the object, 'looks' at it from the back, and responds.)

ROBOT. Goal region is occupied.

MAN. Go to (15, 10) anyway.

(*The robot heads straight towards its target, pushing the obstacle out of its way, and stops in the correct place.*)

ROBOT. Done.

The ultimate purpose of such a machine could be a vehicle or aircraft capable of steering itself from nothing more than a map.

Partnerships of this kind (and I would emphasize that in every respect they are a partnership, a man-machine symbiosis) are now merging in many centres where the necessary computing power is available. They leave no doubt of their capacity to stretch human reason and intuition far beyond its present limits.

One day, not too distant, these partnerships will be commonplace. Whether the side effects of this amplification of our mental capacity prove even more devastating than those of the car on our physical capacity will still depend wholly, however, on the human element in the union. The computer, like the car, will do no more than it is encouraged to do. But the greatest human weakness of all is stupidity, and the computer alone can do nothing about this.

NOTES

CHAPTER ONE

1. *Human Sexual Response* (Little, Brown & Company, 1966).
2. *Human Guinea Pigs* (Routledge and Kegan Paul, 1967).
3. *Science*, vol. 140, 1963, p. 464.
4. Chemical Engineering Progress Symposium Series, vol. 62, no. 66, 1966, pp. 46–64.
5. D'Arcy Wentworth Thompson, *On Growth and Form* (Cambridge University Press, 1966).
6. *Strength of Biological Materials* (Williams and Wilkins, Baltimore [in press]).
7. *Principles of Animal Mechanics* (Longmans, Green and Co., 1873).
8. *Biomechanics and Related Bioengineering Topics*, ed. R. M. Kenedi (Pergamon, 1965).
9. J. P. Paul, *Forces Transmitted by Joints in the Human Body* (Institution of Mechanical Engineers, 1967).
10. B. M. Wright, 'Alcohol, the motorist and the law', in the *New Law Journal*, 1967, June 8th, p. 631, and June 15th, p. 659.
11. *Science*, vol. 113, 1951, p. 292.
12. *Science*, vol. 112, 1950, p. 143.
13. Edholm and Bacharach, *The Physiology of Human Survival* (Academic Press, 1965).
14. *Nature*, February 24th, 1968, p. 770.
15. 1962: Flying 100 yards by Robert Lee Hayes (U.S.) in 7.8 seconds.
16. *Nature*, July 2nd, 1966, p. 89.
17. Wen-Hsiung Ko, 'Microelectronics and Bio-instrumentation', 1966.
18. *Electronics*, February 20th, 1959, p. 49.
19. *New Scientist*, vol. 34, 1967, p. 24.

CHAPTER TWO

1. Stephen Black, *Man and the Motor Car* (Secker and Warburg, 1966).
2. *Spectrum* (Institute of Electrical and Electronic Engineers, March and April 1966).
3. *Scientific American*, October 1964, p. 88.
4. *Naval Research Reviews*, June 1966.
5. *Scientific American*, April 1967, p. 56.

6. *The Computer Age* (Harper and Row, 1965).
7. *International Science and Technology*, May, 1965.
8. *New Scientist*, June 22nd, 1967, p. 706.
9. *Nature*, June 3rd, 1967, p. 975.
10. *Man and His Future* (Churchill, 1963), p. 3.

CHAPTER THREE

1. 'Biolectric control of prostheses', *M.I.T. Technical Report* 446, December 1st, 1966.
2. *Proceedings of the Royal Society of Medicine*, vol. 59, January 1966, p. 1.
3. *New Scientist*, March 12th, 1964, p. 668.
4. *Bio-Medical Engineering*, May 1966, p. 250.
5. *Electronics*, September 20th, 1965, p. 110.
6. *New Scientist*, April 14th, 1966, p. 82.
7. *Proceedings of the International Conference on Sensory Devices for the Blind*, ed. Richard Dufton (St Dunstan's, 1967).
8. *Research Highlights* (National Institutes of Health, 1966), p. 63.
9. *Nature*, February 11th, 1967.
10. *Bell System Technical Journal*, vol. 38, 1959.
11. *Surgical Forum*, vol. 8, 1958.
12. *Scientific American*, March 1967, p. 32.
13. *Bio-Medical Engineering*, November 1966.
14. *The Lancet*, vol. 1, 1966, p. 235.
15. *Science*, January 11th, 1963.
16. *The Lancet*, March 9th, 1968, p. 514.
17. *Transactions of the American Society for Artificial Internal Organs*, vol. 8, 1962, p. 236.
18. *Bio-Medical Engineering*, July 1966, p. 366.

CHAPTER FOUR

1. *Scientific American*, November 1966.
2. *Electronics*, March 21st, 1966, p. 105.
3. David Fishlock, *The New Materials* (John Murray, 1967).
4. *Proceedings of the Royal Society of Medicine*, vol. 46, 1953, p. 647.
5. *British Journal of Plastic Surgery*, vol. 20, 1967, p. 204.
6. *Circulation*, September 1966.
7. *Annals of the New York Academy of Sciences*, vol. 146, article 1, January 8th, 1968.
8. *Research Highlights* (National Institutes of Health, 1966), p. 21.
9. *Textile Industries*, December 1959, p. 130.
10. *Ethics in Medical Progress* (Churchill, 1966), p. 60.

11. *Journal of Bone and Joint Surgery*, February 1965.
12. *Proceedings of the Royal Society*, A, vol. 294, 1966.
13. *Australian Journal of Experimental Biology*, vol. 33, 1955, p. 415.
14. U.S. Patent 3,279,996: published October 1966.

CHAPTER FIVE

1. *British Medical Journal*, November 18th, 1967, p. 410.
2. 'Ethics in Medical Progress', *C.I.B.A. Foundation Symposium* (Churchill, 1966), p. 24.
3. *Surgical Forum*, June 1955, p. 432.
4. *Surgery, St Louis*, vol. 48, 1960, p. 272.
5. *Transplantation*, vol. 4, no. 5, 1966.
6. *Journal of Anatomy*, vol. 77, p. 299.
7. U.S. Patent 3,056,785: October 2nd, 1962.
8. *Journal of the American Medical Association*, vol. 188, 1964, p. 1132.
9. *South African Medical Journal*, vol. 41, 1967, pp. 1265 and 1271.
10. *British Medical Journal*, June 1st, 1968, p. 511.
11. *Spare Part Surgery* (Aldus Books, 1968), p. 163.
12. *The Lancet*, September 14th, 1968, pp. 583 and 585.
13. *British Medical Journal*, November 30th, 1968.
14. *Annals of Surgery*, vol. 160, no. 3, 1964.
15. *Scientific American*, June 1966, p. 94.
16. *The World in 1984*, vol. 1 (Penguin Books, 1965).

CHAPTER SIX

1. *Science Journal*, October 1967.
2. *British Medical Journal*, April 6th, 1968, p. 11.
3. Duncan Davies and Callum McCarthy, *Introduction to Technological Economics* (Wiley, 1967), p. 102.
4. *World Medicine*, March 1st, 1966, p. 34.
5. *The Lancet*, November 9th, 1968, p. 987.
6. *Psychophysiological Aspects of Spaceflight* (Columbia University Press, 1961), p. 345.
7. *Scientific American*, August 1968, p. 66.
8. *Simposio Internationale sugli Omoinnesti* (University of Padua, 1963).
9. *British Medical Journal*, January 13th, 1968, p. 80.
10. *Man and His Future*, ed. Gordon Wolstenholme (Churchill, 1963), p. 217.
11. Paul Bates and John Pellow, *Horizontal Man* (Longmans Green, 1964).
12. *Science Journal*, October 1968, p. 97.